WOULD YOU BUY
A USED SECRET FROM THESE MEN?

Eric Brulard— Conscientious. Dedicated. Speaks seven languages fluently. Won eight field citations for efforts beyond the call of duty. Knows his manual by heart. Never travels without a change of underwear.

Douglas Griffin— Lackadaisical. Easily distracted. Never misses a meal. Women can't resist his penetrating, hint-of-evil gaze. Uses his manual to press his laundry.

Chasing concealed microdots and bomb-throwing anarchists, Brulard and Griffin thud and blunder through explosive mayhem, confusing the Russians, the Chinese, and themselves, in

S·P·Y·S

Donald Sutherland and Elliott Gould as Brulard and Griffin—— You loved them in M*A*S*H when they destroyed the U.S. Army. Wait till you read what they do to the C.I.A.

S·P·Y·S

by T. Robert Joyce

From a Screenplay by
Malcolm Marmorstein
and
Lawrence J. Cohen
& Fred Freeman

SPHERE BOOKS LIMITED
30/32 Gray's Inn Road, London WC1X 8JL

First published in Great Britain by Sphere Books Ltd 1974
Copyright © 1974 by Simon & Schuster, Inc.

TRADE
MARK

ISBN 0 7221 5104 7

S·P·Y·S

Chapter One

THE METRO GROUND to a halt at the Rue St. Denis station and discharged a mixed lot of passengers—housewives, workers, clerks, students, and one American, a tall man with dark curly hair and a camera slung around his neck. This was Douglas Griffin. Griff skipped up the subway stairs and emerged onto the sunny Paris street. His gait was casual, but there was a certain determination in the loose-limbed stride. He was not just out for a stroll.

Ten blocks away was another man on a motor scooter, his moustache and long blond hair masked by the visor of a silver crash helmet. This was Eric Brulard. Even seated, he was as tall as the Peugeots, Renaults and Volkswagens that surrounded him in traffic. Brulard drove just at the speed limit, smiling, but his hands gripped the bars of the scooter more tightly than was necessary. He was not just out for a ride.

Griff checked his watch, looked up at the street sign and turned a corner, unmindful of the faint buzz of a motor scooter somewhere behind him. He rounded another corner and approached a pissoir plastered with old posters advertising the Follies Bergères. A workman in blue overalls came out, straightening his fly, and Griff entered. After making sure he was alone he ran his hand underneath the urinal trough, disgusted by the feel of the slimy porcelain.

Brulard braked his scooter outside the pissoir, checked to make sure he hadn't been followed, and walked inside.

Griff had found the package he was looking for and was pulling away a piece of tape when he heard someone come in. Jumping up, he pretended to be zipping his fly, glanced quickly at the silver crash helmet and went out.

Alone, Brulard knelt down and ran his hand underneath the trough, feeling for the package. The street outside was quiet. Inside the pissoir there was only the sound of Brulard's breathing and the slosh of water in the urinal trough. He touched the package and heard a ticking sound.

Griff had walked across the street to wait. Now he saw the man in the silver crash helmet run from the pissoir and hit the ground. The next moment the pissoir exploded. Its guts—metal pipes, bits of porcelain —flew through the air, jets of water sprayed the street and shreds of Follies Bergères posters rained down like confetti. People streamed out of shops and houses, running toward the wreckage.

The man in the silver crash helmet got up and looked around. His eyes met Griff's and Griff walked away fast.

Brulard, in a rage, threw down his helmet and went after him.

Griff turned a corner, fast, but trying not to attract undue attention. His eyes searched for a place to hide.

Brulard turned the corner after Griff, and found himself in an empty courtyard with one open door and no other exits. He was about to give up his search when his eye caught a movement behind the door. He turned slowly, shrugged as though giving up, then grabbed the open door and slammed it back against the wall.

Griff had been fooled by Brulard's nonchalance and though the door slamming into his shoulder surprised him more than it hurt, a bellow erupted from him.

"Owwww!"

Brulard grabbed his lapels and pulled him from behind the door, his face red with rage.

"Who are you?" he demanded. "Why'd you try to kill me?"

Griff grinned sheepishly and then, as the grip on his jacket relaxed, brought his fist up into Brulard's jaw. Brulard stumbled backward, regained his balance and charged. Griff sidestepped and Brulard smashed into the wall.

Four children came out of the open door and cheered the fighters.

Griff swung, missed, and spun himself around, avoiding Brulard's karate kick.

The children's mother, a stout, no-nonsense-looking woman, rushed out and stood between the two men, jabbering at them in French. Brulard tried to get around her, but by the time he did Griff was sprinting away.

"Thanks, lady," he said, breathing heavily. "You just saved a man's life." He pointed to the alley down which Griff had run. "His."

Brulard parked his motor scooter outside the shabby building that housed the Four Corners Travel Agency and climbed the stairs to the dimly lit agency office. He nodded to a portly, balding man seated behind a desk that bore a sign reading "Mr. Martinson" and walked into the bathroom. Martinson, who seemed surprised to see him, followed him into the bathroom and closed the door. Brulard waited impatiently, hands on hips. Martinson reached behind the toilet paper roll, inserted a key, and the wall next to the toilet slid open.

The two men moved into a room cluttered with travel brochures, maps, leaflets, and film cans. Tattered travel posters and a dusty mirror covered the walls. A 16-millimeter projector sat on a desk in the corner. Martinson closed the door and spun about.

"Why did you come here?" he sputtered.

"They tried to get me, sir," Brulard said flatly.

"What do you mean, get you?"

"With a bomb, sir. While I was making that pickup."

"A bomb!"

Brulard nodded. "The one who planted it got away. But he definitely looked KGB."

"You sure?"

"Yes, sir. He had that demented Russian look."

"But they've been on a nonviolent streak lately," Martinson protested.

"I think it's just me they're after, sir," Brulard said. "I *have* been a thorn in their side."

"We have bigger thorns than you, Brulard."

"Of course, sir," Brulard added hastily. "But they may be smarting from my last trip to Yemen. I was only there a week, and the government fell."

"That was a military coup, Brulard. We had nothing to do with it."

"Didn't we, sir?"

The door flew open to reveal Griff, panting, disheveled, and shouting: "Some schmuck just tried to kill me!" He spotted Brulard. "There he is!"

Brulard fell on him and they struggled, knocking

10

maps and brochures to the floor and kicking up dust.

"He's the one!" Brulard shrieked as Martinson tried vainly to separate the two men.

"Oh, for heaven's sake," Martinson said. "He's with us!"

"What?"

"Let him go!"

Brulard released his grip, and Griff jerked away. "Jesus, where'd you get this goon?"

"You calling me a goon?" Brulard challenged.

"Yeah!"

Martinson stepped between them. "Now both of you. Take it easy."

"What the hell's going on?" Griff demanded. "I was supposed to make a pickup at the pissoir."

"*You* were supposed to?" Brulard said. "*I* was supposed to make it. Next time, read the orders, Junior."

Griff turned to Martinson. "Who is this nut case?"

Brulard threw up his hands. "He calls *me* a nut case. Eight field commendations, Junior . . ."

"Stop calling me Junior."

". . . fluent in seven languages, *Junior*. Top that!"

Griff sneered. "I got laid in the fourth grade."

"That's enough!" Martinson shouted. "Enough! Drop it!" As the two men sulked at each other he added, "Now, Brulard thinks it was KGB."

"I say it wasn't," Griff put in quickly.

"That proves it was," Brulard said.

"Yes," Martinson murmured. "Griff, they could be after him because of that coup in Yemen."

"The only thing is," Brulard said, "I can understand the Russians wanting to kill me . . ." he looked with contempt at Griff, "but why him?"

"It must be that shoeshine stand I knocked over in Bulgaria."

11

"Very funny."

"It wasn't the KGB, Martinson," Griff said, then paused. "I know who it was."

The others stared at him.

"Debug," Griff said.

"Huh?"

"What bug?"

"Come on! Debug this room."

"This room isn't bugged." Martinson was offended. "Where do you think you are? The White House?"

Not dissuaded, Griff reached for a Lufthansa travel poster.

"I suppose there's nothing behind this but a blank wall."

He tore away the poster, revealing a blank wall. Undaunted, he spun toward the film projector.

"And what's this? Just a regular projector? Nothing hidden inside?" He turned confidently to Brulard. "Watch and learn, Junior."

He pulled a side panel off the projector, revealing only the ordinary inside of a projector. Now he whirled around to the mirror.

"How about that thing? If you're gonna use a two-way mirror, you might at least . . ."

He reversed the mirror. It was backed with solid wood.

"Okay, okay. So you just tape everything that's said . . ."

He smiled slowly at the radiator grill. "How many mikes in here?" Jamming his hand behind the grill, he sneered at Brulard. "Wanna guess?"

His hand felt deeper and deeper. His face fell when he pulled out a clump of dust.

"I give you my word," Martinson said. "This room

is clean. No one will ever know what's said in here—
except the three of us."

"I believe you, sir," Brulard said loyally.

"You do?" Griff said. He reached out and opened
the door to the bathroom. A pale man with a fringe of
black hair toppled into the room. The man wore head-
phones attached to a stethoscope-like microphone.

"Damn it, Hessler!" Martinson shouted. "I told you
to stop doing that!"

"I'm sorry," the pale man said. "I thought . . ."

"You're not supposed to think! Out!"

Hessler backed out on his hands and knees. Martinson slammed the door.

"All right, Griff," he said. "Let's have it. Your the-
ory. Who tried to kill you?"

"You did," Griff said simply.

"Ridiculous!" Martinson scoffed. "Why would I try
to kill you two? What makes you think it was us?"

"Technique," Griff explained. "It wasn't the Chinese, because the Chinese are quiet. It wasn't the Russians, because the Russians are neat. It was us. Because we're sloppy. And it was a goddam sloppy job,
Martinson."

"That's no evidence," Brulard said.

Griff ignored him. "Come on, Martinson. Let's have
the truth. Come on. If this room isn't bugged, tell the
truth!"

There was silence for a moment.

Martinson sighed. "All right. It was us."

"I don't believe it," Brulard said immediately.

"It was us," Martinson nodded wearily. "You know
Klein and Stambler? Well, we found out they're working both sides of the street. We had to get rid of
them."

"So?" Griff asked.

13

"So I gave the orders to hit them." Martinson shrugged. "Their code numbers are very close to yours. Hessler got the numbers mixed up. That's how you guys wound up at the pissoir."

"Hessler," Griff muttered.

Brulard was shocked. "Then it had nothing to do with my work in Yemen?"

"It was all a mistake," Martinson explained. "A stupid mistake."

"And a damn near fatal one," Griff added.

"It's okay to be killed in the line of duty," Brulard said. "For one's country." He shook his head. "But a typing error?"

"Don't blame Hessler too much," Martinson said. "He was swamped that day. You know my daughter's getting married. Hessler was sending out the invitations. Oh . . . did you get yours?"

"Well, no . . ." Brulard hesitated. "I didn't . . ."

"Damn mail here. Not like the States. But you are coming to the wedding, aren't you?"

"I suppose. I mean . . . if you . . ."

Griff was amazed. "What are you answering him for? They almost killed us!"

Martinson opened his eyes wide in hurt. "You wanted the truth. I gave you the truth. And this is the thanks I get." He shook his head sadly. "You try to be decent with people . . ."

"Dead is dead," Griff said. "Decent doesn't count when you're dead."

Martinson slapped both men on the shoulder. "I'm going to make it up to you both. I've got a nice soft job for you tomorrow night. Practically a paid vacation."

"What kind of job?" Brulard was suspicious.

Martinson lifted the phone from his desk. "Hessler, bring in the Sevitsky file," he said and hung up. "Now do me a favor, boys. Don't say anything to Hessler. He feels bad enough about this. Believe me."

"He feels bad?" Griff said.

"How do you think I feel?" Brulard said.

"It's a simple enough mistake," Martinson said impatiently. "Just got you mixed up with the other guys. That's all!"

Hessler came in nervously and handed the file to Martinson. As he turned to leave, Griff put his foot out, and Hessler stumbled into the bathroom, ending up with one arm in the toilet bowl.

"Sorry," Griff said. "Just got you mixed up with another idiot."

Chapter Two

ATHLETES FROM ALL over the world were working out in the new Olmypic gymnasium, surrounded by trainers and members of the press. Sevitsky was swinging on the high bar when Griff and Brulard spotted him. Wearing blazers with World-Wide Sports patches and carrying a camera, tape recorder, and microphone, they made their way across the gym until they were so close they could see the beads of perspiration on the Russian gymnast's face.

"He's pretty good," Griff said.

"That's why he won the gold medal twice," Brulard told him.

Sevitsky made a flying dismount and faced the trainers and reporters who crowded around him, asking questions and giving advice.

"I still don't get it," Griff said. "What do we want *this* guy for? A scientist I can understand."

"He wants *us,"* Brulard said. "You know, some people like freedom."

"Sevitsky likes money. That's it."

"You have to put everything down, don't you?"

Griff shrugged.

"How d'you know he didn't fall in love with one of our girls?" Brulard asked. "That would make a great story—Romeo and Juliet on the parallel bars."

"Twenty francs says he's doing it for the dough," Griff said.

"You're on."

Griff hoisted the camera onto his shoulder. "Okay, let's make contact."

Two Russian trainers were eyeing them suspiciously. "Borisenko's men are all over the place," Brulard whispered.

As they moved toward Sevitsky, a middle-aged Russian intercepted them, a young gymnast in tow. "Excuse me," he said, his accent heavy. "American?"

Brulard nodded.

"I am Soviet backward-flip coach. This is Ivan Nabov." The young man smiled. "He win next Olympics," the coach said, patting the boy on the shoulder. "You interview?"

"Maybe later," Brulard said politely.

"I hope soon to visit cousin in your Pittsburgh," the gymnast said eagerly.

"Have a nice trip," Griff said. He tried to walk on, but the coach put a restraining paw on his arm.

"Ivan only one in world who can do double backward flip without landing on head."

"Donovan can do a triple," Griff whispered proudly.

"Donovan?"

"A new guy on our team," Griff said, and as he and Brulard moved on they heard the coach imploring the young gymnast to try a triple for the love of Russia.

"Knock off the crapping around, will you?" Brulard hissed.

They approached Sevitsky, who was being interviewed by a frantic French journalist.

"Excuse me," Brulard said. "We're with World-Wide Sports."

Sevitsky turned away from the Frenchman, looking wary but interested.

"Oh yes," he said, "I've been waiting for you."

He led the two Americans across the crowded floor to the side of the gym. There he turned to them, smiling for the benefit of passers-by.

"You have money and my new Thunderbird?" he asked coldly.

Griff grinned at Brulard. "Freedom, huh?" He held out his hand to collect his twenty francs.

Brulard gave him the money, then shook his head at the greedy look on the Russian's face. "Not on us, Sevitsky. But it's all been arranged. You'll get yours when you get to New York."

Several of the Russian coaches were eyeing them now and Griff busied himself with the camera. Brulard switched on the tape recorder and held the microphone up to Sevitsky.

"How about suede jacket?" the Russian asked.

"What suede jacket?" Brulard said.

"They promise me suede jacket and pants like I see in magazines." Sevitsky was petulant.

Griff came closer with the camera, his movement threatening. "Listen, Sevitsky . . ."

"Also, three appearances on Merv Griffin Show."

"Shut up and listen!" Griff said. "In ten minutes, you go back to the locker room and change."

"The rear door is open," Brulard said. "We'll be parked right outside."

"Will Raquel Welch be in the car?" Sevitsky asked. "Raquel Welch?"

"She is part of our agreement. I see her picture in magazine. We are perfect for each other. I love her."

Grinning, Brulard held out his hand to Griff, who handed him back the twenty francs.

Two English sportscasters approached them. "Ted

Seely here," the first one said, "from International Sports."

Griff turned to him. "Well hello, International Sports. We're World-Wide Sports." He lowered his head and hissed. "What the hell are you guys doing here, Croft?"

The second Englishman hissed back. "I didn't know you and Brulard worked together."

"We don't," Brulard said. "Buzz off."

"Piss off, yourselves," Croft said, turning to the bewildered Sevitsky. "We're upping our offer. That Triumph sports car is yours."

"I have Thunderbird," Sevitsky proclaimed.

"And Miss Yorkshire's dying to meet you," Seely said.

Sevitsky's eyes bulged. "She is?"

Griff jabbed his finger into the Russian's chest. "What about Raquel Welch, you fickle creep?"

Brulard saw the Russian coaches moving a little closer and said, "Cool it, everyone. Let's settle this outside."

"We're not leaving without him," Seely insisted. "I don't know what you've got in your camera, but I know what I've got in mine."

"Don't give me that spy bullshit," Griff said, knocking the camera so it hit the floor, firing a shot that struck the wall near the head of one of the Russian coaches. The coach, a squat hairy man named Grubov, drew a gun and shot, hitting Croft in the shoulder. The Englishman fired as he fell.

"These guys are crazy!" Griff shouted. "What are they doing with guns?"

"I wish *our* camera had bullets," Brulard said wistfully.

"We don't even have film!" said Griff. "Let's go, Sevitsky!"

Dropping most of their equipment, they dragged the young Russian toward the nearest exit. Behind them the gymnasium was in pandemonium. Athletes and newsmen scurried for cover as shots rang out over their heads. Brulard and Griff crawled along the floor, pulling Sevitsky with them, and dived through the door into the hallway.

"I change my mind," Sevitsky said, afraid.

"We made a deal," Brulard screamed. "Now move!"

They ran down the hall and were confronted by two men, unmistakably Russian. Brulard picked up his microphone and pointed it at them.

"Hold it!"

The Russians stopped, confused, then one of them made a motion as if to pull out a gun.

"Don't make me use this thing!" Brulard threatened, brandishing the microphone. The Russians slowly, fearfully raised their hands.

"Turn around and start walking."

Cautiously, the Russians obeyed. Griff grabbed the microphone and spoke into it.

"That's right. Keep moving. Just keep moving . . ."

Brulard and Griff dashed into a locker room, dragging Sevitsky with them.

"Just a little interview," Brulard announced to the roomful of half-dressed athletes. "Nothing to worry about."

"Let 'em interview themselves," Griff said, tossing Brulard's microphone to a man wrapped in a towel.

The door burst open, and the Russians entered, waving their guns. Grabbing Sevitsky, the Americans ran out the back exit into an alley. They cut into a dark side street and ducked into a doorway. After a moment of quiet they heard footsteps running toward them.

"They'll kill me!" Sevitsky moaned.

"Shut up!" Griff said.

They hid in the shadows, holding onto Sevitsky, and saw the Russians round the corner. Spotted by a Russian who shouted to his companions, they jumped out of the shadows and ran up the street, the Russians in swift pursuit.

They ran to the corner, fled down a dark street, turned another corner, and raced down an alley until they came to a low wall. They tumbled over cursing their assignment, and found themselves on a deserted business street.

"I can't run anymore," Griff panted. "We gotta duck in somewhere."

"Right," Brulard said. He took a small tool from his pocket and began jimmying the lock on a men's clothing store, looking around for the Russians.

"You are soft," Sevitsky said. "I could run for miles. It does not bother me."

"Does this bother you?" Griff asked, jamming his elbow into Sevitsky's gut.

Sevitsky smiled. "No."

The clatter of approaching footsteps echoed in the dark. Griff prodded Brulard with his finger.

"Get the goddam door open!"

Brulard jammed the tool in one last time. The lock gave way, but as the three men bolted into the store, the burglar alarm went off. Brulard reached above the door and disconnected the alarm wires, and they ducked behind a counter.

"We can't stay here long," Griff whispered. "They heard that alarm. They'll be here any second."

"We gotta get a car," Brulard said.

"They told me there would be no trouble," Sevitsky complained.

"There wouldn't have been if you hadn't been double-dealing everyone," Brulard said.

"The British come to me," Sevitsky said innocently. "I should have gone with them."

"We ought to throw him the hell out of here," Griff said. "People bleeding all over the place because he wants a car and a suede jacket."

He crawled to the store window and peered out. Four Russians were looking up and down the street.

"We don't have much time," he said. "I'll tell you one thing. I ain't dying for this moron!"

"I know what moron means," Sevitsky said indignantly.

"Good," Griff replied.

"Griffin, we're taking him in," Brulard said. "Martinson's waiting."

"Screw Martinson," Griff said. "Let *him* finish this soft job he gave us."

The Russians were directly across the street, jimmying the lock on another store.

"Won't take them long to find us."

"Let's make a dash for it," Brulard suggested.

"We won't get twenty feet," Griff said.

"It's the only way," Brulard insisted. "Take Sevitsky out the back door. I'll hold 'em off here as long as I can."

"That's nuts!" Griff said. "We'll get our ass shot off."

"Get going, goddam it!" Brulard ordered.

Griff came away from the window and grabbed Sevitsky.

"I never get to America," the young Russian moaned.

"America?" Griff exclaimed. "We'll never get to the back door."

Brulard crawled to the front window while Griff and Sevitsky edged towards the rear exit. Griff opened the back door and saw a car parked in the alley with three Russian agents inside.

Sevitsky took a jacket from the racks and admired himself in a full-length mirror.

"Hey spy," he said. "Look. You think Raquel Welch will like? I want to look nice for her. This fits perfectly, no?"

"Oh beautiful, beautiful. I love it," Griff said. "Let's go."

"I take?" Sevitsky held up the jacket.

"Sure. Help yourself," Griff said and dumped a pile of shirts in Sevitsky's arms. "Terrific stuff. Terrific. Here." He plopped a hat on the young Russian's head. "This'll look good with the jacket. Now come on."

"Is safe out there?" Sevitsky asked, hesitating.

"Yeah," Griff assured him. "Let's go."

"I don't know."

"Stop worrying. By this time tomorrow you'll be driving your Thunderbird." He put his hand on the doorknob. "When I open the door, run straight across the alley. I'll be right behind you." He opened the door and pushed Sevitsky forward. Sevitsky peered out cautiously.

"Get going, you schmuck!" Griff shouted and booted Sevitsky out the door and into the alley. Sevitsky saw the car with the Russian agents and dropped the pile of clothes. The agents jumped out of the car, and when Sevitsky tried to back into the store, Griff slammed the door.

"Comrades. I'm so glad you're here. They make me do it. They forced me. They hurt me. They——"

The Russians surrounded him and forced him into the car. Griff heard the slamming of a door and the car drove off.

From his post at the front of the store, Brulard saw the Russians jimmying the lock in the store next door. A car pulled up, the men on the street got in and the car drove away. Brulard started for the back of the store just as Griff was coming up front.

"What's going on?" he asked. "They're all leaving. Where's Sevitsky?"

"He panicked," Griff said. "He said he wanted to go back to Russia. I tried to stop him but——"

Brulard's fist slammed into his mouth, and Griff stumbled back against a display case.

"Of all the times to go chicken!" Brulard screamed. "Giving him up without a struggle."

"I'm not dying for a money-hungry acrobat," Griff said.

They left the store and walked in silence to a telephone booth where Brulard dialed Martinson's home number.

"My career was unblemished until this," he said as the phone rang. "Unblemished!!!"

Martinson was not sleeping, nor was he alone in his bed. He leaned across one of the two girls on either side of him and picked up the phone.

"Hello, sir," Brulard said in a calmer tone. "I'm sorry to disturb you. This is . . ."

"I know who it is," Martinson said impatiently.

"I thought you'd want to be informed, sir. That special VIP junket to New York . . ."

"I've heard the whole story," Martinson said. "The police version. And Washington will have got it by now. How much did the Russians pay you guys?"

"Sir!" Brulard said. "I object to that implication and I demand the right to be heard. I'm sure that when Griffin tells you . . ."

"Is Griffin with you now?" Martinson asked.

"If we could come over now, sir?"

"No, impossible," Martinson said, looking at the two women in his bed. "Up to my ears in work here. Ummm . . . how long will it take you to get to your place?"

"Twenty minutes, sir," Brulard replied.

"All right, wait for me there. Understand?" He hung up without hearing a reply, his forehead a mass of angry lines. Bare arms reached up from both sides of him and smoothed his skin.

"Boobala," the women cooed in unison.

"Oh shut up!" he said and picked up the telephone to make another call.

Chapter Three

IT WAS CLOSE to midnight when the men approached Brulard's apartment building in a run-down section near Montmartre.

"When Martinson gets here," Brulard said, worried, "you tell him the truth . . . just the way it happened."

"Truth . . . lies . . . I've been in this racket so long, I don't remember the difference."

Brulard opened the door to the building and they started up the staircase.

"Anyway, I've had it," Griff continued. "I know of so much crap that's going on, I can't sleep. I resign."

"Good."

"You're the first to know."

They came to the first landing, and Brulard pulled out his keys.

"So quit!" he said. "But my career isn't going down the drain because of you." He inserted the key in the lock, having some difficulty because of the dim lights in the hall. "I have eight field commendations . . . I'm up for promotion . . . I . . ."

As the key turned in the lock, Griff heard a faint buzz. He grabbed Brulard by the shoulders and flung him across the landing, diving after him. A tremendous explosion from inside the apartment blew the door across the hall. Brulard sat up, staring into the smoke.

"What the hell?"

"I think you've just been fired," Griff said. They bolted down the stairs, out of the building, and across the street.

"It doesn't make sense," Brulard said breathlessly.

"Nothing makes sense," Griff echoed.

"But they spent fifty thousand dollars training me . . ." he said nervously. "They wouldn't try to finish me with a three-dollar bomb. I've got to see Martinson."

"Better not let him see you first," Griff warned. "It's wet stuff for us. Get that through your head."

Brulard was silent, then nodded his head. He motioned for Griff to follow and they clung to the sides of buildings, jumping from shadow to shadow, constantly checking to make sure they weren't being followed.

Brulard led Griff into the deserted courtyard of an old apartment building. The windows that looked down on it were dark.

"This where we're holing up?" Griff asked.

"No," Brulard said resentfully. "Go home, will you?"

"You think my place *isn't* booby-trapped?" Griff asked.

Brulard dismissed the idea. "Yeah, well . . . stop following me."

"I can't," Griff replied cheerfully. "I saved your life. I'm responsible for you."

He followed Brulard across the courtyard to the rear stairway and watched as Brulard took a pocketknife from his pants and pried loose a board from the third stair.

"Is there enough room for both of us?" Griff said.

Brulard grunted, reached under the board and pulled out a small leather valise.

"Gee, you spies know all the tricks," Griff said.

"At least I know where I'm sleeping tonight," Brulard said and opened the valise, revealing a stockpile of shoes, socks, underwear, a flashlight, and an electronic coding machine.

"What'd you do?" Griff asked. "Knock off a Woolworth's?"

Brulard filled his pockets quickly. "The manual tells us to keep one of these in every major city we operate in."

"You read the manual?" Griff exclaimed.

Brulard stared at Griff with a mixture of amazement and contempt. "I don't know how the hell you ever got into the organization."

Griff shrugged. "It was either that or the Salvation Army."

Brulard ignored him and continued stuffing his pockets.

"How about some underwear for me, sir?" Griff asked.

Brulard sighed and handed him a pair. Griff bowed in gratitude and stuffed it in his pocket.

"Comrade," he said.

Brulard slammed the suitcase shut and replaced it under the stair. When the stairboard was back in place, they left the comparative safety of the courtyard for the uncertainty of the streets.

Chapter Four

THEY STOOD IN the shadows, and Brulard pointed to the shabby apartment building across the street.

"Her name is Sybil," he said. "She's an anarchist."

"How'd you ever meet an anarchist?" Griff asked, impressed.

Brulard looked up and down the deserted street and motioned for Griff to follow him.

"Remember last year, those anarchists who blew up the American Embassy?"

"Yeah," Griff replied.

"I sold them the dynamite," Brulard said.

Griff stopped in disbelief. "You helped blow up your own embassy?"

"We got the ringleaders and that's what counts," Brulard said as they reached the entrance to the building. Griff shrugged, and they walked inside.

"Let's get our stories straight," Brulard whispered as they mounted the stairs. "She thinks I'm an out-of-work American."

"She's right," Griff said.

"And she doesn't know my real name."

"What is your real name?" Griff asked.

"What's yours?"

They exchanged a quick smile and continued to the second floor in silence. Griff followed Brulard to the door at the end of the hallway and watched him knock.

"Also," Brulard whispered. "She's crazy about me."

"Figures."

They waited for a reply from inside and when none came Brulard knocked again. "Sybil?"

There was a shuffling sound from beyond the door and a sleepy female voice spoke.

"Who is it?"

"Eric," Brulard said.

"Eric who?" was the sleepy reply.

Brulard's face fell but he plugged on. "You know— *Eric!*"

After another pause, the girl spoke again. "Oh, Eric. Just a minute."

Inside, the walls of the apartment plastered with political posters, Sybil had apparently been wide awake. She and two companions, the big-jawed and lanky Gaspar, and Paul, wiry as a welterweight, were frantically hiding the gelignite, wires, detonators, and timing devices they had been working on. Sybil pulled off her sweater and slacks and threw on a robe. Amidst the flurry of activity, she ran again toward the door.

"I'm coming, Eric," she said, using her sleepy voice, and then went back to stashing the bomb equipment. Gaspar dumped a coil of wire into the closet, scooped up the last bits of evidence and ran into the bedroom. Paul opened the refrigerator and hid some gelignite behind a pile of soggy lettuce.

Out in the hallway, an impatient Brulard was instructing Griff on proper behavior around anarchists. "Just keep quoting Kropotkin and you'll be all right."

"Kropotkin? Who's Kropotkin?"

"He was a famous anarchist," Brulard said as the door was opened. Sybil, sleepy-eyed, her long brown hair in disarray, was leaning against the jamb.

"Eric!" she exclaimed, throwing her arms around Brulard's neck, then leading him into the apartment. "It's been almost two months. Where have you been?"

"Oh, lots of places," Brulard replied evasively. "Looking for answers . . . you know."

"Yes, I know," Sybil said. "And have you found any?"

"Just me," Griff said from the doorway.

"Ah . . . this is my . . . ah . . . pal . . ." Brulard told Sybil. "Ernest."

Sybil guided Griff into the apartment and shook his hand firmly. "Hello, Ernest."

"Any friend of Eric's . . ."

"Ernest's out of work too," Brulard interrupted. "He's an authority on Kropotkin."

Sybil turned back to Griff, her interest piqued. "You are?"

Griff looked down at the floor and shuffled his feet. "Well, I wouldn't say an authority . . ."

"Some time you'll have to tell me all about it," Sybil said and turned to Brulard. "And where have you been . . ." She moved toward the door to usher them out. "Some other time."

"Sybil," Brulard said, moving in front of her. "I've . . . I've been looking forward to this."

"Yeah," Griff said. "We thought maybe you'd put us up."

"No, no," Sybil said, surreptitiously glancing toward the bedroom where she knew Paul and Gaspar were still hiding. "That's impossible."

"I just got into town," Brulard said wearily. "I'm dead."

"Damn near," Griff muttered.

"No, I can't!" Sybil said, gesturing to the front door. "What would the neighbors think?"

33

"They've seen me here before," he said.

Sybil shook her head insistently, then noticed that Griff was headed for the refrigerator.

"No!" she shouted, running across the room. She slammed the refrigerator door closed but Griff had already had enough time to appraise its contents.

"There's nothing in there," she said, smiling.

Griff shrugged. "How about a little ham and dynamite on rye?"

Sybil's smile fell and panic crossed her face. She looked searchingly from Griff to Brulard.

"Is he one of us?" she asked.

"I told you," Brulard said. "He's my pal."

She hesitated, gave Griff a slow once-over, and opened the refrigerator door. Griff took out as much food as he could carry in both hands.

"All right," Sybil said. "You can stay in here tonight. But you must leave first thing in the morning."

"*He* will," Brulard said.

"Excuse me for not being more hospitable," Sybil said, opening a closet and pulling out blankets and a pillow. "But it is late and I must be up early." She dumped the bedding on the frayed sofa. "You don't mind the couch, I hope."

"*He* doesn't," Brulard said.

Griff gestured pontifically with his sandwich. "As Kropotkin said . . . one man's couch is another man's roller skates . . ."

Brulard stared at him, confused, while Sybil tried to recall where Kropotkin had said that.

"In any case," she said to Brulard. "I'm glad you're here."

Brulard beamed expansively and winked at Griff.

"We need some more explosives," Sybil said and walked to the bedroom door. "Good night, Ernest."

"As Kropotkin said—may all your dreams be comedies," Griff replied.

"I've always loved him for saying that," she said and closed the bedroom door behind her.

Brulard spread the blankets on the couch, muttering to himself.

"Look," Griff said. "I'm sorry as hell."

"You should be," Brulard grumbled.

Griff went to the cupboard and took out bread for another sandwich. "I mean about coming here tonight. I shouldn't have. You were right."

"I usually am."

"I should know by now," Griff said as he prepared the sandwich. "Not that it happens every time. But nine times out of ten."

"What in the hell are you talking about?"

Griff shrugged and pointed to the bedroom.

"What about her?" Brulard demanded.

"You mean you didn't see it?" Griff asked.

"What?"

"The way she looked at me," Griff said. "Jesus, as soon as I stepped through that door she started raping me with her eyes."

"And that's as close as you'll ever get," Brulard warned.

"I didn't encourage her, did I?" Griff asked innocently. "I mean, you saw it. I didn't turn it on. That's just how I affect women. Honest, a guy introduces me to his wife, and his marriage is never the same. Like tonight . . ." He interrupted himself to take a mammoth bite of his sandwich. "You said she was crazy about you. And maybe she was. Then I walk in and . . . poof!" He pointed to the couch. "Flip you for it."

"You can have it," Brulard said in disgust.

"Where you gonna sleep?"

"I'll manage," Brulard said, walking to the bedroom door. "And may all your dreams be nightmares."

He entered the bedroom, closed the door behind him, and stood still while his eyes adjusted to the dark.

"Is that you?" Sybil asked.

"It's okay," Brulard whispered. "I can see."

He moved toward the outline of the double bed, banging his shin on a chair and cursing under his breath.

"Please," Sybil said. "I'm so tired."

"So am I," Brulard replied.

He reached the foot of the bed, sat down and pulled off his shoes.

"Don't," Sybil implored.

"You know me," Brulard said. "Fastest undresser in the West."

He pulled up the edge of the rumpled blanket and tickled her bare foot.

"Stop it!" Sybil squealed, laughing.

"Still ticklish, huh?" Brulard said, tickling up her leg.

"Noooo! Please stop!" she shrieked, pulling her foot away.

Brulard pulled the blanket up further and tickled her other foot.

"Tickle, tickle, tickle."

By the dim light that came through the window, he saw that the foot he was holding was larger and hairier than Sybil's. He looked up the leg and saw Gaspar next to Sybil, his long body looking threatening in the faint light.

"I . . . uh . . . Hi," he said and grabbed his shoes, backing away from the bed. "We were just kidding around, you know. For old times' sake . . . like brother and sister . . . uh . . . sorry if I woke you up. I was just looking for the bathroom."

Keeping his eye on Gaspar, he backed up to the bathroom door, opened it and saw Paul shaving at the sink in his underwear, a straightedged razor in his hand.

"Uh . . . my mistake," Brulard said, smiling and backing out of the bathroom. "Don't mind me. Uh . . . goodnight. Everybody." He pulled open the bedroom door and slunk out.

Griff was comfortably propped up on the couch, munching away contentedly on his sandwich. "It's like I told you," he said. "Don't take it too hard. It's just one of those things."

"That's right," Brulard agreed, shrugging. "I wouldn't have believed it but . . ."

"Nine times out of ten," Griff reminded him.

"Well, it happens. She's all yours."

Griff took another bite of ham on rye. "Soon as I finish my sandwich."

"I told her I'd send you right in," Brulard said.

Griff dropped the sandwich on the coffee table, stood up, and headed for the bedroom door.

"You sure you don't mind?"

"Why should I?" Brulard asked and as he watched Griff enter Sybil's bedroom, his face broke into a satisfied grin. He took a bite of Griff's sandwich and waited for the explosion in the bedroom. After the second bite, his grin faded and he tiptoed to the bedroom door. He pressed his ear against it but there were no sounds. He crouched to peer through the keyhole but there was no keyhole, so he got down on his hands and knees and squinted through the crack at the bottom of the door, but he still couldn't see anything.

He stood up and knocked at the door. There was

no answer. Furious now, he went back to the coffee table and picked up Griff's sandwich, deliberated, then hurled it out the window, wishing Griff and his big mouth were as easily disposed of. Then he flopped down on the couch, crossed his arms over his chest, and stared at the closed door.

Chapter Five

EARLY THE NEXT morning a meeting took place that was to have serious effects on the lives of Griff and Brulard. Yuri Borisenko, handsome, sad-eyed Russian agent, entered a dimly lit restaurant, blinking in the unaccustomed gloom, and adjusted his black arm band, while glancing about. He spotted Martinson sitting in a corner and crossed the restaurant to that table.

"Good morning, Yuri," Martinson said, rising and smiling at the Russian.

Nodding coldly, Borisenko said, "Good morning, Lester," and sat down.

The waiter approached and Borisenko pointed to Martinson's orange juice.

"I had them save you a fresh piece of melon," Martinson said. "It's delicious."

"I am not interested in melons this morning. Coffee," he told the waiter. "Black."

When the waiter left, he turned to Martinson and pointed to his black arm band.

"I have just seen off on an Ilyushin airliner two coffins," he said bitterly. "Two of my best men, shot down in their prime—in a lousy gymnasium."

"I'm sorry about that, Yuri," said Martinson.

"Sorry is not enough!" he whispered, pounding his fist on the table. "Moscow is very upset."

"So's Washington," Martinson muttered.

"I remind you of our reciprocal agreement of '72,"

Borisenko stated. "A corpse for a corpse. You owe me two, Lester."

Martinson nodded and sipped his coffee. "It was taken care of last night." He looked at Borisenko, expecting praise.

"Not true!" Borisenko exploded. "The blast last night was a phony—bloodless."

"*What?*" Martinson stared into his coffee. "Hessler must have goofed again."

"Last month," Borisenko said with pride, "when one of our men killed your courier by mistake, he was eliminated within the hour."

"No one knows that better than I," Martinson said. "You shot that son of a bitch on the spot! That's what I call leadership!"

Borisenko leaned back and toyed with the black arm band. "So just remember, Lester. If you don't take care of it . . . I will."

"Don't push me, Yuri," Martinson said. "I'll handle it."

"Soon," Borisenko warned.

"The only thing is . . ." Martinson stopped when the waiter brought Borisenko's coffee. "He said black!" Martinson screamed. "You know what black is? BLACK! BLACK!" When the shaken waiter had gone, Martinson continued. "The only thing is . . . I'm a little short of field men right now . . ."

"I want the two men responsible for mine," Borisenko demanded.

"But our agreement of '72 doesn't specify that," Martinson protested. "All I owe you is two dead American citizens."

"And who did you have in mind?" Borisenko asked. "Maybe Elvis Presley and Valter Cronkite?

Maybe Spiro Agnew and Steve McVeen?" He lowered his voice and leaned towards Martinson. "Or maybe your daughter and the boy she's marrying?"

"You have a great sense of humor, Yuri."

"I like a good joke," Borisenko said, smiling, waiting for his threat to sink in.

"Now Yuri, we don't want another bloodbath like '70, do we?" Martinson said reasonably. "Why ruin everything? Let's be humane about this. We'll kill Brulard and Griffin. You don't have to." He waited for some sign of approval from Borisenko. "All right?"

Borisenko was silent until he saw Martinson break out in a cold sweat, then he smiled and looked at the menu.

"Now! What is for breakfast?"

"Yuri, I wish I could invite you to the wedding," Martinson said as they both studied their menus. "But . . . well, you understand."

"Of course," Borisenko replied. "But would it be all right to send a little anonymous gift?"

"Certainly," Martinson said, flattered and pleased.

"Do they have a sterling silver samovar?" Borisenko inquired.

"Not yet."

"You approve of the one she's marrying?"

Martinson shrugged, saying neither yes nor no, but implying no. "Well, what can you do?"

"I know," Borisenko said. "They don't make them like us anymore, eh?" He laughed and punched Martinson's shoulder playfully.

"That's right," Martinson said and punched him back.

As they laughed, a hidden camera and microphone

41

recorded their meeting. Later that day, the entire conversation would be replayed for the edification of four rather impassive Chinese gentlemen who were not amused.

Chapter Six

BRULARD WAS SLEEPING peacefully on Sybil's couch while Borisenko and Martinson were meeting to decide his fate. The bedroom door that he had stared at so furiously the night before opened slowly, and Paul and Gaspar tiptoed into the living room. As they passed Brulard, Gaspar lifted the American's jacket and went through the pockets, rejecting the socks and underwear, until he came to the passport. He flipped it open expertly and motioned for Paul to copy down the number. When this was done, the two young Frenchmen replaced the items in the pockets, draped the jacket back over the chair, and making sure that Brulard was still asleep, left the apartment.

The bedroom door soon opened again and Griff tiptoed into the living room. Glancing to see that Brulard was asleep, he reached inside the jacket, located the wallet, and helped himself to a few francs. Replacing everything carefully, he left the apartment. Brulard sniffled in his sleep and turned over.

Far away, in an elegant section of Paris, pigeons cooed in cages atop an expensive apartment building. Lafayette ran his pudgy fingers over the head of his favorite bird, murmuring encouragement, and sent the bird flying. The pigeons were essential to his work and he knew he was fortunate to get an apartment with a rooftop area large enough for his coops.

Smiling expansively, Lafayette watched the bird disappear in the distance. The door to the terrace opened, and Griff came out. Lafayette turned at the sound and his pleasure vanished.

"Lafayette," Griff said. "I'm here."

"Oh no . . ." Lafayette said, looking about for an escape. "Not you."

"You owe me, Lafayette," Griff said, advancing as the pudgy man retreated.

"Go away!" Lafayette said, shooing Griff as if he were a bothersome bird. "The word is out on you."

"How bad is it?" Griff asked, stopping his approach.

"Go away, please," Lafayette implored. "I don't want bloodstains all over my roof." He mustered his courage and attempted to walk past Griff to the door of his apartment.

"Come on," Griff said, blocking his way. "Give me five thousand so I can get away."

"Five?" Lafayette exclaimed. "For what? You have nothing to sell." He tried again to reach the door but Griff held his ground.

"How about the real story on Afghanistan?" Griff offered.

Lafayette shrugged, unimpressed. "Who cares?"

"OK," Griff said. "The whole new NATO defense setup."

"It was in *Time* magazine yesterday," he sighed. Before he could move Griff grabbed him by the collar.

"I mean it," Griff threatened, pushing the fat man toward the edge of the roof. "I'm desperate. Five grand or . . ." He looked meaningfully at the six-story drop to the ground below. "Or I outlive you."

"Five couldn't take you far enough," Lafayette choked. "You're dead, Griff. To save yourself would take . . ."

"How much?" Griff demanded, pressing the fat man closer to the edge. *"How much?"*

"Half of what I can get for what Lippet is carrying," he said, looking down at the street then back to Griff. "Two hundred thousand . . . split down the middle."

"Knock over the great Lippet?" Griff said, intrigued.

"You could do it, Griff," Lafayette assured him. "A hundred grand for you. What do you say?"

"Where's Lippet now?" Griff asked.

"He's making the pickup in London," Lafayette said and breathed a sigh of relief when Griff let go of his collar.

London, Griff thought. London and the great Lippet. London and the great Lippet and half of two hundred grand.

Brulard had finally awakened, put on his rumpled clothes, including the much-rifled jacket, and ransacked Sybil's explosive-filled refrigerator for breakfast. He gathered some eggs and set a pot of coffee brewing. Sybil came out of the bedroom in a robe and Brulard growled a greeting.

"Good morning," she said cheerfully and opened the window. "What a lovely day."

Brulard growled at her again but she merely smiled and pointed to the coffee pot. "Could I have some?"

Brulard slammed a cup onto the table and with a sigh of exasperation, poured the coffee.

Sybil sat and sipped it, looking at Brulard over the edge of the cup.

"What's the matter?"

"Kinda crowded in there last night," he said.

"Oh," Sybil said airily. "Gaspar is an old friend."

"How about the guy in the loo?"

"Paul? He is a *new* friend."

"You make friends easily."

"Yes."

"So, where do I fit in?"

Sybil shrugged and sipped her coffee. "You were a good friend. Then I do not hear from you for two months."

"What do you mean?" Brulard demanded, sitting down opposite her. "I wrote."

"One postcard," she said. "What are you so mad about?"

"What do *you* think?"

"I don't know," she replied. "You tell me."

"All right," he said assuming a getting-down-to-business tone. "I come back—after two months—and I bring my pal to meet you . . . and he isn't even in the door when you start . . . when you start raping him with your eyes."

Sybil seemed pleased. "I did?"

"I'll say. If they gave jail sentences for eye rape, you'd have got twenty years."

"Well . . . he *was* fascinating last night."

"I'll bet," Brulard grumbled.

"We were Kropotkining until it got light."

"That's a new name for it."

"Ernest made it up," she told him. "Quoting Kropotkin is Kropotkining."

"I suppose he quotes while he makes love," Brulard said angrily.

"Makes love!" Sybil exclaimed. "You and your horrible bourgeois expressions. One does not *make* love. One loves . . . one is loved."

"Don't change the subject!" Brulard shouted.

"You brought it up!" she shouted back.

"Do you want some more coffee?" Brulard shouted again.

"Yes!!!!"

Brulard snatched her empty cup, refilled it, and sat down at the table. They remained silent, staring at their coffee.

"Would you like to know what is attractive about him?" she asked.

"No."

There was a silence again until Brulard's curiosity got the best of him.

"What's so attractive about him?"

"He has . . ." Sybil's hands made vague gestures in the air. "How can I describe it . . . a sinister quality. There is something going on behind those big, soulful eyes."

"His eyes aren't so big," Brulard said.

"Most people . . . their eyes are like open windows . . . but his . . ."

"Listen," Brulard said. "And I'm being completely objective . . ." He held up his left hand and stuck his pinky out. "There's more sinister quality in that little finger . . ."

Sybil laughed and shook her head.

"There is," Brulard insisted. "I'm telling you."

"Then that's why I'm so attracted to you too," she said, still laughing.

Brulard smiled for the first time and leaned across the table to her. "So how come you never rape me with your eyes?"

She stood up abruptly, backing toward the couch in mock retreat.

"What do you think I'm doing now?"

Brulard let out a yip of joy and dived on top of her as she fell back onto the couch.

"Nooo," she cooed. "Ten-der-ly." She barely had time to say the word before Brulard kissed her. "Darling?" she whispered, running the tip of her tongue along his ear.

"What?" he asked, nipping at her neck.

"Can you get me some more dynamite?"

"As much as you want," he murmured and grabbed a lush handful of flesh at her hip.

"Mmm."

"Mmm."

Griff burst through the door shouting: "Hey, let's go!" He crossed briskly to the couch and tugged at Brulard's jacket sleeve.

"Where?" Brulard asked, confused. "What?"

"Come on," Griff spoke excitedly. "We've got to get to London!"

Brulard looked at him, then back at Sybil. Something told him that Sybil would wait and that London wouldn't.

Chapter Seven

GRIFF AND BRULARD flew at once to London. By the next afternoon they had located Lippet and were tailing him down Regent Street where he walked leading a tiny brown-and-white dog on a silver leash. Keeping to the other side of the street, they watched him stroll into a jewelry store.

"He might be making a pickup," Griff said.

"Just shopping," Brulard disagreed. "I don't know about this. No one touches Lippet. We knock him over and we'll have everyone looking for us."

"He carries nothing but top of the line. Do you know what he got for that Polish Secret Police file? We could live forever on that."

Lippet came out of the jewelry store, looking like any distinguished businessman, and continued up the street with his dog. Griff and Brulard followed, slowing their pace to keep a safe distance behind him.

"We're taking a helluva chance," Brulard said.

"We're gonna have to hole up somewhere for a long time. That takes money."

"Maybe I should go to Washington and see the old man. He'll straighten this out. I still don't get——"

"There's nothing to get," Griff interrupted, and seeing Lippet get into a cab, he pulled Brulard by the arm and hailed one himself. "Come on. We're gonna lose him!"

Their cab followed Lippet's, and when he and his

dog got out in front of Dunhill's, the two men resumed their surveillance across the street.

"Do you know where you're going to head for yet?" Brulard asked.

"I don't know. Maybe South America."

"I think I'm going to Iceland."

"That's a good idea," Griff mumbled, his eyes on the door of Dunhill's.

"Sybil going with you?" Brulard asked.

"What?"

"Never mind. Uh . . . when you came in on us, we weren't doing anything. Don't worry about it."

When Griff did not reply Brulard changed his approach.

"She's really changed."

He waited again for Griff to react and again got silence as Griff studied the store across the street.

"I don't know what's happened to her. She's not as much fun as she used to be."

"Funny," Griff said, turning to him. "She didn't say that about you."

"What did she say about me?"

"She likes you very much. But there is . . . one thing."

"What?"

"That you talk too goddam much!" Griff exploded. "Shut up for five minutes."

They looked at each other in silence for a moment, then Brulard raised his hand tentatively, as if asking permission to speak.

"Griff . . ."

"What is it now?"

Brulard gestured timidly over Griff's shoulder. "There goes Lippet."

Griff spun around to see Lippet already halfway down the block.

"Jesus!" Griff muttered, grabbing Brulard's arm and pulling him along. "Jesus."

For the next few hours, becoming increasingly bored and tired, they followed Lippet and his dog through a series of expensive shops. As evening came, master and pet swung through the revolving doors of an elegant hotel restaurant. After what seemed a reasonable time, Griff and Brulard followed and took a table across the room.

The restaurant was a richly appointed, wood-paneled room, with thick carpets and glistening silver. Griff was forced to sit with his back to Lippet.

Lippet ate methodically. His dog was perched on the chair beside him, paws on the table. Brulard watched the waiter pay great deference to it.

"That dog's practically human," Brulard said.

"What's so great about being human?" Griff asked through a mouthful of food.

Brulard shrugged and continued eating, keeping one eye on Lippet. "He's a wino," he announced.

"Lippet?"

"The dog."

Griff turned around to see Lippet holding a glass of wine up to the dog's mouth. The dog sniffed it, testing its bouquet, and licked delicately at the glass.

"If there's anything I hate," Griff said, turning away revolted, "it's a smart-assed dog."

"Now he's cutting up his food," Brulard said.

"The dog?"

"Lippet."

Griff peered around again and saw Lippet feeding bite-sized pieces of veal to the dog.

"Disgusting," he said, and turned back to his own plate.

"What you got against dogs?"

"Nothing. I just don't like to see them eating in good restaurants, that's all."

People at the adjoining tables turned to stare at him, and Griff lowered his voice. "Well, do you think it's right?" he continued. "That mutt eating veal scaloppine when forty percent of the world's starving."

"Twenty-three percent."

"And drinking expensive wine," Griff muttered. "A dog doesn't have the palate."

"Something's up."

A bellboy approached Lippet's table with the bill and spoke to him. Lippet signed the bill, picked up the dog, and left the restaurant.

"Be right back," Griff said and followed him into the lobby of the hotel.

Lippet was seated on a couch with two other men, one an Arab. Griff got into a telephone booth, pantomiming a conversation and keeping an eye on Lippet.

The three men talked and laughed quietly, and the Arab took an envelope from his robes and handed it to Lippet. Lippet excused himself and carried the envelope to the desk clerk who put it in the safe. Lippet joined the other two men, and the trio left the hotel.

Griff raced out of the booth and back to the table where Brulard had just taken one of his lamb chops.

"Didn't want to waste 'em," he explained. "They were getting cold. Want 'em back?"

Griff sat down. "He did it."

Brulard put the lamb chop down and looked seriously at Griff. "When do we hit him?"

"As soon as we can. He just met the Beirut contact.

When I was black-bagging that run, I was carrying stuff worth forty, fifty thousand . . ."

"How do you know that?"

"What do you mean, how do I know? I looked."

"That's against regulations," Brulard said stiffly. "You weren't supposed to look."

"I don't believe you," Griff said in amazement. "Martinson goes through your mail every day and you're afraid to look in his bag?"

"I wonder if he's carrying for Martinson."

"Who cares about Martinson? I want the money."

"I care about Martinson! I'm going to nail him! I was the only one in the Paris office with eight citations . . ."

"You told me, you told me."

"Why does he want to kill me? Just last week he told me himself—'Brulard, you'll be a field director in . . .'"

"Jesus!" Griff interrupted impatiently. "Are you in or out?"

"I'm in, I'm in," Brulard assured him. "I'm gonna get Martinson."

"Good," Griff said and pushed the bill toward Brulard. "Here. Take care of this. I owe you."

"I can't pay for this. Don't you have anything."

"Do you think I'd order a meal as expensive as this if I was going to pay for it? I thought you took money from your suitcase."

"I don't keep money in my suitcase. Someone might steal it."

"How're we going to pay for this?"

"You figure it out," Brulard said and pushed the bill back. "You wanted to come here, not me."

"This kind of trouble we don't need . . ." Griff mumbled, toying with his cigarette lighter.

"Why'd this place have to be so expensive?" Brulard moaned.

Griff shrugged and pointed the cigarette lighter across the table. He pressed the underside of it and a fine mist sprayed into Brulard's face.

"What are you doing?" Brulard exclaimed, waving his hands to keep the mist away. Too late he realized what the spray was.

"That's LS-10!"

"You'll be okay in fifteen minutes," Griff assured him.

"That stuff'll . . ."

Brulard tried to say more but the LS-10 had taken effect and he gagged, rocked back and forth in his chair, gasping for breath before finally falling over backward. The stunned diners watched him twitch and writhe on the floor, legs quivering, arms flailing. He clutched at the tablecloth, upsetting everything on the table with a great crash.

"Waiter! Waiter!" Griff shouted. The man came to their table, his face a mask of concern.

"What is it?" he asked in alarm.

"I don't know!" Griff shouted. "Something he ate! What kind of a restaurant is this?"

"Please, sir," the waiter said. "I'll call a doctor."

"I'll take care of him myself!" Griff said as he helped Brulard stand up.

Brulard, still gasping and trembling, hissed in his ear. "I'll kill you for this!"

Griff dragged the unsteady Brulard toward the exit.

"This is going to cost you a pretty penny!!!" he shouted at the waiter. "Look what you've done to him."

Brulard's face and body were still contorted, but in the fresh air the effects of the drug began to wear off.

"Damn you!" he gasped as Griff continued to pull him down the street. "I had money in my shoe . . ."

"That'll teach you to lie. God's punishing you."

Staggering down the street, his mind still foggy, Brulard was in no condition to question Griff's methods. One thing was clear. No matter what the friction between them, they had to stay together to get Lippet, because that was the only way they would stay alive.

Chapter Eight

THE SURVEILLANCE OF Lippet continued the next morning, and surprisingly led to the ferry heading back to France.

While Brulard called Sybil to arrange for transportation on the other side, Griff was hidden behind a newspaper, watching Lippet and his dog drinking coffee in the ferry café until they finished and walked toward the landing area, joining the stream of boarding passengers.

Griff's impatience grew as Lippet bought a ticket and boarded the ferry. He ran to the ticket office and bought passage for two. Just then Brulard appeared.

"He just got on," Griff said. "Let's go."

"Everything's okay with Sybil. She told me she'd meet us with a car."

"Good. That's going to make things a little easier."

"But it's crazy going back to Paris," Brulard said. "We're asking for it."

"Wherever Lippet goes—we go."

"But Paris!"

"Lippet is going to get us out in style," Griff said, dragging the reluctant Brulard toward the ferry.

"By the way," Brulard said. "Sybil said she was looking forward to seeing you. I told her I'd tell you."

"Fine. Let's go."

"She also told me that she was looking forward to seeing me."

"That's wonderful."

The ferry crew was casting off, but Brulard held Griff back.

"Look," Brulard said. "I had to tell Sybil something about you."

"What'd you tell her?"

"I told her you were married."

"What the hell you tell her that for?"

"You needed a cover," Brulard explained. "I gave you a good cover."

"Thanks," Griff said, then saw that the ferry had begun to move.

"Come on!!!"

He pulled Brulard and they made a frantic fifty-yard dash, having to jump on deck just as the ferry pulled away from shore.

Their embarkation was observed by Mr. Chang, a Chinese gentleman already on board. He had watched them with the same detachment he displayed earlier viewing the film of Martinson and Borisenko.

The ferry moved slowly over the choppy waters of the English Channel with Brulard and Griff at the rail.

"When do you think's the best time to get him?" Brulard asked.

"When he goes to the john."

"What if he doesn't go to the john?"

"Then we'll make him go."

"How? How we gonna make him go?"

"With this," Griff said, taking a small comb from his pocket. "You ever see one of these?"

"No."

"What's your clearance?" Griff asked, holding back the comb.

"Top secret."

"Top secret and you never saw one of these?"

"No. What does it do?"

"You touch someone with it, and they have to go peepee."

Brulard stared at the comb and when Griff touched his hand with it, he jumped away.

"Watch it!" he cautioned, then saw the smug look on Griff's face. "Very funny."

"Relax, will you?" Griff said. "If we don't get him with the peepee comb, we can always shoot him with your cuff links or something."

They left the railing to look for Lippet, found him in the rear seating section, and took up their post where they could keep an eye on him.

"I've been thinking about something, Griff. How come you want me along?"

"I don't know."

"You don't really like me, do you?"

"I never said that."

"You didn't need me to pull this off," Brulard said. "How come you didn't dump me in London?"

"Okay, I'll tell you. Because you helped me out. You got me out of paying a big restaurant bill, you found me a place to stay in Paris, you gave me a set of underwear—which, by the way, I can't find. I couldn't get along without you."

"Come on, Griff. Let's have the truth, for once."

"All right. You really want to know why I wanted you along?"

"Yeah. Why?"

Griff lowered his eyes and whispered. "Because you're so much fun to be with."

After an initial moment of puzzlement over this remark, Brulard smiled. Then he laughed. Griff couldn't help but join him.

"I guess I am kind of uptight sometimes," Brulard admitted.

"You and that chickenshit suitcase," Griff laughed. "You're dynamite!"

"You know something? My name's not really Brulard."

"That's all right. My name's not Griffin."

This admission of mutual deception sent them into another fit of laughter. Griff was the first to regain control and as he did, he took out his comb and touched Brulard with it. Brulard laughed harder, but Griff's face had become serious.

"I'm not kidding this time," he said.

Brulard saw Lippet heading for the men's room, leaving his dog on the seat. They followed him, just as the French side of the Channel came into view. Time was short.

When they entered the men's room Lippet was drying his hands. They closed the door and made sure no one else was there.

"Let's have it, Lippet," Griff demanded. "The envelope."

The startled Lippet turned to them, then reached into his pocket for a pill and popped it into his mouth. Griff and Brulard jumped him, prying his jaws apart.

"No, you fool!" Brulard screamed, then turned to Griff. "Don't let him bite it!"

"Jesus," Griff said, his hands on Lippet's jaw. "He must be carrying big!"

Lippet fell to the floor, taking Griff and Brulard with him. Both had their fingers in his mouth, probing for the pill as Lippet tried to swallow it.

"Get the pill!" Brulard said.

"No!" Lippet croaked. "No!"

"Got it!" Griff shouted in triumph, tossing the pill to the floor.

"You don't understand," Lippet gasped. "Heart trouble . . . glycerin."

"Oh Jesus," Brulard muttered. He reached inside Lippet's jacket for another pill and tossed it into Lippet's mouth.

Lippet's breathing became more regular and they lifted him to his feet.

"Easy now," Brulard cautioned. "Easy."

"You feeling better?" Griff inquired.

"Yes," Lippet said as he threw a fast punch that caught Griff on the temple. Griff fell back but Brulard slammed Lippet against the wall. As he crumbled, Brulard caught him and propped him up on a toilet seat.

"Think he's all right?" Brulard asked.

"He's still breathing," Griff said, reaching into Lippet's inside pocket and withdrawing the envelope. He opened it and began reading.

"I'll take that," a voice commanded from behind.

A giant of a man was standing at the bathroom door with a gun in his hand.

"Who're you working for?" Griff asked.

"Mr. Lippet," the man said. "Get him up. Bring him to."

"You work for him," Griff said. "You do it."

Without flinching, the man fired a shot that shattered the plaster near Griff's head.

"Get Mr. Lippet up!"

Griff and Brulard remained immobile. The giant fired another shot that hit the sink between the two men and ricocheted crazily around the bathroom, lodging finally in Lippet's chest as he struggled to his feet.

"Nice shot," Brulard said.

"Oh boy," Griff said. "Are you gonna get it."

Taking advantage of the man's stunned condition, Brulard jumped him, grabbed the gun and knocked him to the ground with a karate chop to the neck.

They left the bathroom, closing the door tightly. Just then Lippet's dog scampered to the bathroom door where he began scratching and yipping. Brulard ran back and scooped the dog up in his arms.

"Nice boy," he murmured, stroking the dog's head.

The ferry had landed and they were stuck with the dog.

Chapter Nine

THEY PUSHED THROUGH the crowd and looked for Sybil.

"Get rid of that mutt," Griff said.

"I can't do that. He's got no place to go."

Sybil waved to them from the dock and motioned behind her to a brand new Peugeot. They waved back and pushed on until they reached her.

"Where have you been?" she asked.

"Never mind," Brulard said. "Let's get going."

"What is this?" Sybil asked, touching the dog's head.

"A present," Griff said, looking nervously at the disembarking passengers. "Let's go!"

Sybil got in the back of the car and Brulard followed, surprised to see Gaspar already there and Paul at the wheel. Griff got in front, slammed the door, and waited for the car to move.

"Let's go!" Griff said. "Let's move!"

"Not yet," Paul said calmly. "I'm warming the engine."

Brulard looked out the window to see if they'd been followed. "Come on! It's warm enough!"

"Not quite," Paul said. "It's the break-in period."

"What break-in period?" Brulard asked.

"It's his father's new car," Sybil explained, patting Paul's shoulder reassuringly. "He has to be careful."

"We can't wait here," Griff told Paul. "Come on! Step on it!"

"*We* are giving the orders," Gaspar said.

"Then tell him to get going," Griff pleaded. "We're in trouble."

"Yes, you're in trouble," Sybil agreed, thrusting a gun in Brulard's ribs while Gaspar stuck one in Griff's neck.

"What the hell are you doing?" Brulard exclaimed, as the car began moving at last.

"We found out about you," Sybil said, the gun steady.

"What are you talking about?" Griff demanded.

No one answered and they drove slowly out of the ferry traffic and onto a country highway.

"Didn't I get you the dynamite to blow up my embassy?" Brulard asked Sybil.

"Yes," Gaspar replied. "And our leaders were captured."

"It's no use, Eric," Sybil said. "We know you both work for the CIA."

"The CIA?" Griff exclaimed. "Us? That's a good one."

"We have an inside contact," she said. "He checked your passport number . . . and both your fingerprints."

"So what?" Brulard said.

"Maybe he's a fink for them," Griff suggested.

"That's right. Besides, CIA guys *never* leave fingerprints," Brulard affirmed.

"Let's shoot them now," Gaspar said.

"No, listen," Griff implored. "Wait a . . ."

Paul slowed down the car, and Griff looked behind to see if any cars were following them.

"What are you stopping for?" he asked, as he felt increased pressure from Gaspar's gun.

"I heard a rattle," Paul said, cocking his ear to the sound of the motor.

"Look for it later," Brulard said.

Paul shook his head and slowed the car still more. "My father told me to write down all the rattles."

"Paul," Sybil said, "keep driving." Brulard turned to her and smiled a thank you. "And look for a side road where we can kill them."

"Sybil, listen to me," Brulard pleaded.

"Save your breath."

"For what?" Griff asked. He took a cigarette, and Gaspar jerked it out of his mouth.

"No smoking. You could burn the seats."

They drove in silence. The dog on Brulard's lap was the only one who enjoyed the ride. The road behind them had been empty until a Citroën came into view.

"There's a side road up ahead," Paul said.

"Good," Sybil replied, turning around.

"A car's behind us. Slow down and let it pass."

Paul slowed the car and signaled for the Citroën to pass.

"Listen," Brulard said. "You're making a big mistake."

The Citroën pulled alongside of the Peugeot and the driver waved his arm out the window.

"He's waving me to stop," Paul said as the man leaned further out, waving his arm wildly.

"Hessler!" Griff gasped, recognizing the little man from Martinson's office who had mistakenly tried to blow them up in the pissoir.

"Speed up!" Brulard shouted, poking Paul in the shoulder. "Step on it!"

"Maybe he wants directions," Paul said.

"He wants to kill us!" Griff yelled. He moved toward Paul but Gaspar's gun was jammed deeper into his neck.

"None of your tricks," Gaspar warned.

"Pull over, Paul," Sybil said.

As Paul's foot moved toward the brake, Griff forced his own foot on top, flooring the accelerator. The Peugeot jerked ahead, leaving the Citroën in a cloud of road dust. Paul tried to lift his foot, but Griff pinned his arms.

Brulard grabbed the steering wheel from behind. The sudden movement caught Sybil and Gaspar off guard.

"Sixty!" Paul groaned when he looked at the speedometer. "Oh my God. Shoot them, Gaspar."

Gaspar tried to point the gun but the car swerved and jolted so much he couldn't get off a shot.

Two shots rang out and Gaspar looked amazedly at his cold gun. The back window had been hit in two different places, shattering the glass, and Hessler's Citroën was closing in.

Brulard made the car weave and careen across the road. Griff kept his arms locked around Paul's shoulders and his eye on Hessler.

"He's aiming for the tires."

"The Hi-Speeds!" Paul moaned. "They cost extra!"

"Faster," Brulard told Griff.

"It's down to the floor now."

Brulard cut sharply to the left, throwing everyone further off balance, then sharply to the right, until they veered off the road, bouncing crazily.

"Let me go," Paul grunted, struggling against Griff. "I'll kill you! I'll kill you!"

Brulard forced the car back onto the road. He saw

in the rear-view mirror that Gaspar was leveling the gun, released one hand from the wheel, and struck the Frenchman's wrist hard. Gaspar dropped the gun and it went off, shattering the stereo system.

"Shit," Paul said.

Brulard swerved off the road toward a high stone wall, banked by an enormous pile of hay.

"Hold on," he said as he forged through the haystack, scattering hay wildly. Brulard urged the Peugeot back onto the road and turned to see the Citroën slam into the stone wall. Hessler jumped free as the car exploded.

"All clear," Griff said, watching the flames. "We made it."

"You can have your car back now," Brulard said to Paul, letting go of the wheel.

Griff released the boy, dusting off his lapels and smoothing his jacket sleeves. "There you are . . . hardly a scratch."

"Give me your gun," Paul said to Sybil, facing around. "Let *me* shoot them."

"Watch out!" Gaspar shouted, but it was too late. The Peugeot smashed into the back of a Volkswagen that had stopped at a crossroads.

They all emerged unhurt, but Paul in a rage ran to the other car, Gaspar bringing up the rear. Two enormous men leapt from the tiny VW and advanced on them menacingly. Brulard and Griff bade a hasty farewell to Sybil and the dog, and dove into the brush alongside the road.

Brulard looked back at Sybil with some regret, but took solace in knowing that their passport to freedom, Lippet's letter, was safe on their fleeing persons.

Chapter Ten

GRIFF AND BRULARD strained to read the letter over Lafayette's shoulder in his pigeon-infested living room.

Dear Sir:
    In regard to your lost parcel, please be advised that we have put a tracer on it. All correspondence should refer to reference number A-225-SOL.

It continued, but Lafayette had seen enough. He held the letter steady and scraped the punctuation off with a scalpel, then lifted it with a tweezers and placed it on a microscope slide. A series of numbers and letters appeared when it was magnified. Lafayette nodded his head.

"Mmm."

"Mmm, good?" Griff asked. "Or mmm, bad?"

"Mmm, so-so."

"I thought you had a deal," Brulard said to Griff.

"We have. Two hundred thousand, split down the middle, right, Lafayette?"

Lafayette shook his head noncommittally. "Mmm."

"I don't like that mmm," Burlard said.

"I'm afraid I have overestimated," Lafayette said, shrugging helplessly. "I thought Lippet was carrying bigger."

"Look you fat gangster . . ." Griff threatened, holding Lafayette by the collar.

"Hands off. My pigeons are armed. Antoine!" he signaled to a pigeon perched on the couch. "Shit on his head!"

The bird took off and circled the room. Griff and Brulard automatically covered their heads.

"Okay," Griff said. "What's your top offer?"

"Wait a minute," Brulard said. "I want to know what's on those things."

"No, that is not part of the bargain," Lafayette said.

"How much, Lafayette?" Griff asked.

"For you . . . five thousand."

"Bastard!" Brulard spat.

Lafayette put the microdot back in the envelope and handed it to Griff. "If you think you can do better elsewhere . . . Think it over and decide."

He opened the door and stepped out onto the roof. When he was out of sight he opened one of the coops and selected a pigeon. Glancing back furtively he took a tiny packet from his pocket, tapped the contents of it into a small capsule and tied it to the pigeon's leg.

Griff and Brulard remained inside debating.

"I don't know," Brulard said. "You trust that guy?"

"About two inches on a clear day," Griff said looking more closely at the envelope. "Hey, how much punctuation did he take off that letter?"

"Three periods, two commas, and a semicolon."

Griff held the envelope open. "Only the periods are here."

"That son of a bitch!" Burlard said as they ran onto the roof.

Lafayette cuddled the pigeon in both hands and didn't seem frightened to see them.

"Lafayette!" Griff shouted.

"Don't!" Burlard said.

But the warning did no good, and the next instant the bird was in the air.

"You've made up your minds?"

"You double-crossing bastard!" Griff yelled.

"I'll get it," Brulard said, racing around the roof, trying to grab the low-flying bird.

Griff charged Lafayette and grabbed him by the throat.

"Call it back," he said, pressing harder.

"I can't."

Brulard cooed at the bird, lunged for it, and sprawled on the ground empty-handed.

"Bring it down," Griff said again, applying more pressure to Lafayette's throat.

"All right," Lafayette choked. "Claudine! Come to daddy."

As they looked up at the pigeon, two gunshots rang out and Lafayette went limp in Griff's arms. Another shot hit the wall near Griff's head and he dived to Brulard, knocking him out of range.

"The goddam pigeon *is* armed," he said incredulously as the pigeon flew away.

"On your feet!" came a familiar voice, and they turned to see Lippet's immense bodyguard standing in the doorway of Lafayette's apartment, a gun in his hand.

"The guy in the john," Brulard said.

"And keep your hands up. High!"

As they raised their hands and stood, Griff looked down at Lafayette.

"What'd you kill him for?"

"Maybe I was aiming at you," the man replied.

"You aim at me," Brulard said, "you kill Lippet."

"You aim at me," Griff said, "and you kill Lafayette. You're a great shot. You got him for a bodyguard, and you don't need an enemy."

"Shut up! Shut up! Both of you!"

He moved along the parapet, edging toward them,
gun pointed.

"Where's Archie?" he asked.

"Archie?"

"He thinks we're going to tell him where Archie is,"
Brulard said.

"Ha!" Griff said, going along with Brulard's game.

The man fired another shot that bit the tar at their
feet.

"Listen," Griff said. "Archie's fed up with you. He
says you're always shooting the wrong people."

He fired another shot, chipping a piece of wall near
their heads.

"I'm just gonna ask once more . . ." he warned,
sliding closer.

Griff and Brulard saw a hole in the parapet that
the big man didn't see.

"Should we warn him?" Brulard asked Griff.

"He'd never believe us."

"For the last time," the man said. "Where's that
goddam . . ." He reached the hole, lost his balance,
and tumbled over the roof. The last word of his sentence rang out. ". . . dog?"

Griff and Brulard ran to the edge of the roof and
looked down at the body splattered on the pavement.

"Archie?"

"Archie!"

They bolted through Lafayette's apartment and
down the stairs. They had to get the dog they'd left
with Sybil.

"I told you Lippet was carrying big," Griff said.

72

"The stuff on the pigeon is probably in code."

"And the key to the code's on the pooch."

"And we haven't got either of 'em," Brulard concluded gloomily.

"What we have to do," Griff said, "is get the bird and the dog, then the code, then the money, and then we're free."

They dashed from Lafayette's building directly into the arms of four bruisers who awaited them. Their shouts were muffled as they were shoved unceremoniously into a parked limousine. The men jumped in, locked the doors, and drove off.

Brulard and Griff were on their hands and knees on the floor of the back seat, dazed and frightened. The sliding door dividing the driver's compartment from the back seat slid open to reveal Hessler's face glaring at them.

Chapter Eleven

THE SETTING COULD not have been more peaceful—birds singing in the trees, a gently rushing river by a wide open field, a narrow country road bordering the water. Martinson stood in the river in full fishing regalia, a rod and reel in his hands. The limousine pulled up behind him.

Griff and Brulard were dragged out and shoved down to the river bank.

"Look what I caught, sir," Hessler called out to Martinson

"Your luck's better than mine," Martinson said. "I can't get a bite. Not a nibble." He turned and smiled at Griff and Brulard. "Good to see ya', fellas."

"Cut the crap, Martinson," Griff said.

"What's the matter? I'm glad to see you. I've been trying to contact you all week."

"Yes," Brulard said angrily. "And we know how, sir."

"You're still calling him 'sir'?" Griff asked in amazement.

"I've got good news for you," Martinson told them. "You're both up for promotion."

"Promotion, hell," Brulard said. "You've been trying to kill us."

"Don't be silly. Why I think of you boys like I think of my prospective son-in-law."

75

"How many times you tried to blow *him* up?" Griff asked.

"Do you know what they're talking about, Hessler?" he asked the stubbornly silent Hessler. "See? You think I'd want to lose a man with seven field citations?"

"Eight," Brulard corrected.

"Seven *languages,*" Griff said. "Fluently."

"That's what I mean," Martinson said. "You fellas are indispensable."

"Maybe it was a mistake," Brulard said to Griff. "I'll bet it was all that idiot Hessler's idea."

"What do you want, Martinson?" Griff asked.

"Nothing. Just what you took from Lippet."

"You don't think we'd be stupid enough to have it on us, sir?" Brulard asked.

"Stop calling him 'sir.' "

"The letter, boys," Martinson ordered, extending his hand.

They were surrounded, so Griff handed over the letter. Martinson scanned it greedily, tossing his fishing rod to Hessler.

"There seems to be some punctuation missing," Martinson said.

"Two commas and a semicolon," Griff agreed.

"And you wouldn't be stupid enough to have those on you?"

They shook their heads sadly.

"Suppose I told you a lot of freedom is riding on the information Lippet was carrying?"

"Then we'd say it must be worth a lot of loot," Griff said.

"Wait a minute," Brulard whispered to Griff. "If it's people's freedom . . ."

"Shut up!" Griff shouted.

"Okay," Martinson said, handing the letter back to Griff and repossessing his fishing rod. "I'll contact Washington and make you an offer."

"Tell them the price is high," Griff warned.

"Don't overplay your hand, boys. Remember that you still have relatives in the States." With that final warning, he turned around and cast his line into the river.

"All right, Hessler," Brulard said. "Drive us back to town."

Hessler just stared at them.

Griff and Brulard walked quickly along the country road, keeping to the river side.

"I told you Lippet was carrying something big," Griff said breathlessly. "As long as we've got it, we're safe."

"Only we haven't got it."

When they heard a car behind them they turned quickly, thrusting out their thumbs for a hitch, but the car drove by.

"The punctuation stuff is code," Griff said. "So the key to the code must be on the dog. We've got the dog. Sybil does. So all we need is that pigeon."

They heard another car and again stuck out their thumbs. The black limousine passed them, then slowed to a stop. As they trotted toward it, a second limousine with a man leaning out the window waving to them came up behind. It was Borisenko's second-in-command, Grubov.

They were driven around the next bend, where the hip-booted Borisenko stood in the river, casting with greater skill than Martinson.

"Hello, boys," he called out when they were brought to him at gunpoint. "Won't you join me?"

"Are you kidding?" Griff asked.

"You join him," Grubov said, prodding them from behind with his gun.

Griff and Brulard walked into the freezing water.

"It is more private here," Borisenko said.

"Why can't you use a padded cell like everybody else?" Brulard asked.

Borisenko responded to a tug on his line and expertly reeled in a squirming fish.

"How's that?" he asked.

"Terrific," Griff muttered.

"No wonder Martinson can't catch anything," Brulard said. "He's being upstreamed."

"I am always a little up the creek from Martinson," Borisenko stated, unhooking the fish. "I understand you boys have something to sell."

He extended his hand and Griff gave him the envelope. He glanced over the letter and looked up.

"This is all?"

"There's some punctuation missing," Griff said. "See?"

"Two commas and a semicolon," Brulard added.

Borisenko crumpled the letter and tossed it back to Griff.

"Okay," Griff said. "We've already got a customer."

"Have you?" Borisenko asked, opening his fishing basket and taking out a pigeon.

"Claudine!" Brulard exclaimed as Borisenko released the bird.

"No!" Griff shouted, churning through the water after the pigeon. He soon tired and turned back to Broisenko. "You nut! Why did you . . . ?"

Borisenko smiled and held up the message capsule.

"Two commas . . . and a semicolon," he said as he opened the capsule and tapped its contents into the river.

"Don't!" Brulard shouted, diving after the punctuation.

"Leave it," Griff said, pulling him back up.

"I think I spotted them!"

"Jerk!" Griff yelled. "You want to drown for a semicolon?"

"And a fake one too," Borisenko said.

"See," Griff said. "He knows the punctuation's only a decoy."

"We have to get up early to fool you," Brulard said, shaking himself like a wet dog.

"Then you know what was on the commas and semicolon?" Borisenko asked, suspicious.

"Sure," Brulard said.

"Basketball scores," Griff guessed.

Borisenko looked carefully at them and shook his head. "Quotations from fortune cookies."

"That's right," Brulard said. "The basketball scores were on the question mark."

"Enough of this!" Borisenko said. "Where are the real microdots?"

"That's our secret," Griff replied.

"You will get them for me," Borisenko threatened.

"Nope," Brulard said.

"How much you willing to pay?" Griff asked.

"We're selling to Martinson," Brulard said loyally.

"We're selling to the highest bidder," Griff corrected.

"Martinson," Brulard stated adamantly.

"Even though he tried to kill you?" Borisenko asked.

"Martinson wouldn't do that; he's like a father-in-law to us."

"Then ask him about the reciprocal agreement of '72—a corpse for a corpse. He owes me . . . two."

"We're selling to the highest bidder," Brulard said nervously. "You'll get your chance."

"That is all I ask," Borisenko replied graciously. "I take my chance. You take your chance. Now I bid you good day, gentlemen."

He turned away and cast his line into the water. For the moment they were safe. Setting out for Paris on foot, they reasoned that all they had to do was find the dog and stay out of everyone's way.

A few miles further upstream, the Chinese agent Chang stood hip deep in the river, casting his line. Having seen Borisenko and Martinson's restaurant conference, and Griff and Brulard's ferry scene with Lippet, he listened carefully to the device in his ear that broadcast Borisenko's conversation. He didn't want to miss a word.

Chapter Twelve

GRIFF AND BRULARD huddled in a doorway across from Sybil's apartment.

"Remember," Griff said. "Whatever Borisenko offers to pay—we ask double."

"Providing we have the microdots."

"We will have."

"Providing they're on the dog."

Griff moved cautiously to look up at Sybil's apartment window.

"They gotta be. Lippet's bodyguard practically said so, didn't he? And they weren't on the pigeon."

"Next question. How do we get to the dog?"

"What does the manual say?"

"It says, when faced with an impossible situation—bluff."

"Figures," Griff muttered and took a deep breath. "Let's go."

They left their hiding place, crossed to Sybil's building, and ascended the stairs slowly, hesitating when they got to her door. Griff knocked very gently.

"If they get tough," he said, "let me soften up Sybil."

"Yeah. Use your big soulful eyes . . ."

"My what?"

The door opened and Sybil stared at them in disbelief.

"What d'ya say?" Griff said.

Inside Gaspar sat at the table, busily making a bomb. A small mimeograph machine turned out inky pieces of paper. As soon as they entered Gaspar drew his gun.

"Don't move!"

"Who's moving?" Griff asked.

"Hands up! UP!!"

Griff raised his hands and turned a soulful gaze on Sybil. "Sybil," he murmured passionately.

"Shoot them!" she said to Gaspar, and headed for the copier.

"Wait a minute!" Brulard said. "Look, we didn't have to come here."

"We wanted to square ourselves with you," Griff said.

Sybil speeded up the machine, drowning out their words.

"You've got us all wrong!" Brulard yelled.

"That's right. As Kropotkin said . . ."

Sybil sneered at Griff, turned to Gaspar and gave him the nod. "Go ahead."

"No!!!" Griff implored.

"Listen!!"

Sybil motioned to Gaspar and he lowered the gun.

"The truth is . . ." Brulard said desperately. "We . . . ah . . . we *used* to work for the CIA."

"That is . . . we pretended to . . ."

"That's right . . . we pretended to work for them in order to get the inside dope on 'em."

Sybil stopped the machine. The silence was overwhelming.

"Keep talking," she ordered coldly.

"Well . . . that guy shooting at us in the Citroën is CIA," Griff said.

"They found out we were spying on them. We know

too much. We could tell you all kinds of things about their operation."

"We could tell you where their secret headquarters is, so you could blow it up."

"All right," Sybil challenged. "Tell us."

"Okay," Brulard replied, thinking furiously. "It's . . . um . . . well, you know the supermarket down near the . . ."

"It's the Four Corners Travel Agency," Griff said. "Just check it out."

"We don't have to," Sybil said.

"See," Griff told her. "That proves you can trust us, doesn't it?"

"By the way, where's the dog?" Brulard asked casually.

"Shut up!" Gaspar shouted and raised the gun. "Turn around and keep your hands up."

"Sybil," Griff murmured as she switched on the machine again.

"Wait," Brulard called out. "We know lots of other things."

"And there's something else . . ."

"Money!"

"That's right. Lots of money."

Gaspar hesitated and looked at Sybil. With a decisive movement, she stopped the machine and crossed her arms.

"Look at you," Brulard said. "Sweating over a lousy mimeograph machine. You could have modern equipment, a printing press."

"Two printing presses," Griff added.

"I don't trust them," Gaspar said.

"Fifty thousand francs," Griff said. "That's what we can get you."

"For the cause!" Brulard said.

"They're stalling," Gaspar said.

"A hundred thousand. Cash!"

"From two out-of-work Americans?" said Gaspar contemptuously.

"Where would you get that kind of money?" Sybil asked.

"We'll have it in a few days," Griff told them. "What have you got to lose by waiting?"

"Paul should have a vote in this," Sybil hesitated.

"Paul!" Gaspar called into the bedroom. "Come in here. The dog's bath can wait."

"Bath!" Brulard screamed as he and Griff dashed for the bathroom.

"Don't move!" Gaspar warned, brandishing his gun. "Don't move."

Griff and Brulard ignored the bullets spewing from Gaspar's gun into the door frame.

"Paul! Wait!" Griff shouted.

"Hold everything!" Brulard screamed, as a bullet shattered a bedside lamp.

In the bathroom Paul held the dog above a tub filled with sudsy water. Griff burst into the room and snatched the dog. Immediately he bumped into Brulard, knocking Paul into the tub. Brulard grabbed a towel and followed Griff.

"Easy," he cautioned Griff. "Don't rub anything off."

He spread the towel on the bed and Griff placed the dog carefully on top.

In the living room, Sybil struggled over the gun with Gaspar.

"Where do we look first?" Brulard wondered.

"Follicles! Search his follicles."

They parted the dog's hair, picking at the roots, as a bullet shattered the mirror above the dresser.

"We sure could use a magnifying glass," Brulard

said, as the next wild bullet took a knob off the bed-post.

"How about his tail?" Griff suggested. "Does it look real to you?"

"Hmm. I don't like the way it wags."

"Me neither. Check it out."

As Brulard examined the dog's tail, Sybil and Gaspar lurched into the bedroom. Paul finally pulled himself from the bathtub.

"Maybe it's in one of his teeth," Brulard suggested.

"Right," Griff said and went for the dog's mouth. "Look for lead fillings."

Griff pried open the dog's mouth just as a soapy Paul appeared in the doorway of the bathroom. He hoisted a chair and staggered toward the bed, but collided with Sybil and Gaspar. All three slipped on the trail of soapy water.

Griff looked into the dog's mouth and drew his head back, repulsed. "This mutt eats nothing but garlic."

"Want to change places?" Brulard asked, lifting the dog's tail.

Chapter Thirteen

A FEW MILES outside of Paris, in a small country church, Martinson walked down the aisle with his tall, blond daughter, Ellie, rehearsing for the wedding. The giggling bridesmaids walked behind, followed by the restless groom, Alan, his long hair drooping on his forehead.

The verger walked backward down the aisle directing the procession.

"That's right. In time with the music," he said, nodding his head and waving his arms as if conducting.

Martinson spun around and hissed at the bridesmaid directly behind him. "Don't stand behind me. I don't want anyone standing behind me."

"Heads up, everybody. No smiling . . . but look happy. Now . . . you stop here . . . and the *padre* will do the rest. Thank you everyone."

The verger smiled and bowed from the waist, and the group of people split apart.

"Daddy, it's going to be beautiful," Ellie said, kissing her father's cheek. "If only mother could be here to see it."

"Yes," Martinson said. "She would've liked it very much."

"Couldn't we invite her?"

"I told her she could come. But *I'm* not paying her air fare."

"But you're a travel agent," Ellie suggested reasonably. "You could get a discount."

"Not for her!" Martinson declared righteously. "She likes New York so much, let her stay there."

"Right," Alan commented idly.

"Nobody asked you," Martinson growled.

"I mean, what's the difference anyway?" Alan asked. "It's only another ordinary wedding."

"*We*," Martinson huffed, putting his arm around his daughter, "are not ordinary."

"Daddy, we *are*. Alan's right."

"Now listen, Ellie. You listen to me," Martinson said and took her hands. "You can't always go by appearances in this world. There's more to some of us than meets the eye."

"Cliché time," Alan said.

"Just remember, Ellie. Your father isn't as unimportant as he seems."

"Of course you're not," Ellie said reassuringly.

"No one could be," Alan said.

"Now look here, you little. . . ."

"Daddeeee!"

"Stop daddying me!"

"But Daddy, I don't care that you're not important. It's not important."

"I *am* important!" Martinson shouted impatiently. "I can't tell you why or how, but I am. You take my word."

"Okay," Alan said. "You're a very important travel agent."

"I'm more than that!"

"Daddy, there's nothing wrong with being a travel agent."

"I know there isn't," Martinson agreed. "But I'm MORE!"

S·P·Y·S

The verger approached silently and tapped him on the shoulder. "Pardon sir. There's a a gentlemen . . ."

He pointed to the rear of the church. The doorway seemed empty but as Martinson looked, Hessler's face came into view.

"Maybe one of your tour groups is missing," Alan suggested.

"A lot you know," Martinson said and hustled down the aisle toward Hessler.

"What's wrong? What are you doing here?" he asked angrily, leading Hessler outside.

"Borisenko made contact with Brulard and Griffin," Hessler said.

"I don't like that. Don't like that at all, Hessler."

"They got something off Lippet."

"But what? You don't think it's about 'Crossroads,' do you?"

"I don't see how, sir. But it could've been 'Fusebox.' We had a leak on 'Fusebox.' "

"That's right. 'Fusebox.' And what about 'Switchblade'?" We had a double agent on 'Switchblade.' "

"No, not on 'Switchblade,' " Hessler corrected. "That was 'Fireplug.' "

The brooding Martinson nodded, then a thought struck him and his face lit up with relief. "Wait a minute! Wait a minute! What are we getting so alarmed about? Why should we assume it's about us?"

"Because it usually is, sir," Hessler said.

"That's right. It *is* always about us. What should I do now?"

He paced up and back, muttering to himself.

"After all I've done for those two guys . . ."

"Let's move in on them," Hessler suggested. "Hit them hard."

"No. Just keep watching them."

89

"Daddeee!" The wedding party poured out of the church, posing for Alan's home-movie camera. Ellie beckoned for her father to join them.

"In a minute, darling," he called out.

"Alan wants to take some movies . . ."

"Coming!" Martinson shouted and turned to Hessler. "That lousy Alan . . . you'd better start a dossier on him.

He moved back toward Ellie. "Where do you want me, kids?"

Things were quieter in Sybil's apartment but the air was still thick with suspicion and mistrust. Griff sat next to the dog, his concentration broken by the ripping sound of Brulard tearing apart the dog's collar.

"Nothing," he said, holding up the shreds.

"If only he could talk," Griff said, staring into the dog's eyes.

"Inside his ears?" Brulard suggested.

"I looked. But it's gotta be on him."

"It isn't."

"But the guy on the roof said . . ."

Both men thought for a moment, trying to recall the bodyguard's exact words.

"What *did* he say?" Brulard asked. "He didn't say that it was on him."

"That's right. He just wanted the dog."

Brulard ran his hand over the dog's head, smiling fondly. "He could be a linkup . . ."

" . . . to whoever's got the microdot," Griff concluded. He grabbed the dog and they rushed into the living room.

The anarchists were seated at the table, and Gaspar raised his gun.

"We've taken a vote," Sybil said.

"Kill them," Paul hissed.

"Two for . . ." Sybil said. "And one against."

"Kill them now," Paul whispered fervently, but Sybil ignored him.

"You have exactly three days to deliver us one hundred thousand francs."

Griff and Brulard hesitated for a moment, then nodded assent. They knew they had to agree to her terms or face Gaspar's gun.

Chapter Fourteen

THEY BORROWED TWO uniforms from the concierge of Sybil's apartment building, the blue cotton work suits of Parisian laborers. Brulard topped his off with a cabbie's cap, Griff with a bandanna around his forehead. Brulard unleashed the dog, and they waited for him to lead them.

"Go, boy, go," Griff said encouragingly, but the dog remained rooted to the spot.

"Come on," Brulard said. "Take us to your contact."

The dog looked up at both of them but still did not move.

"Maybe he can't get his bearings," Griff said. "He doesn't know this area."

Brulard nodded and kneeled before the dog, pointing up the street. "Arc de Triomphe, that way."

Griff stooped over and pointed in another direction. "Place Pigalle . . ."

"The Louvre," Brulard said, pointing one way. "Flea Market," pointing another.

At Brulard's last suggestion, the dog did an abrupt about-face and trotted off in the opposite direction.

"Figures," Griff said.

They followed after the dog, staying a few yards behind him, not wanting to crowd him. The dog romped through the streets, sniffing at various things. The men could barely keep up the pace.

Finally the dog ran up to a frizzy redhead in a see-through blouse who was leaning against a building, hip thrust out provocatively, and began nipping at her heels.

"Beat it, Rover," the prostitute said out of the side of her mouth. "I'm working."

A workman came out of a café and she smiled, but he kept walking. Griff and Brulard approached her and she turned on her most seductive pose.

"Lippet sent us," Griff panted.

The prostitute wrinkled her face, trying to place the name.

"Lippet?"

"He's dead," Brulard said.

"Lippet? Dead? Oooo."

"Very sudden," Brulard said and snapped his fingers. "Like that."

"Poor Lippet," the woman said sympathetically.

"But his last words were that we were to get it from you."

"It will cost you eighty francs," the prostitute said, reverting to business.

"Eighty?" Brulard exclaimed.

"Inflation," she replied. "Everything has gone up. I'm no exception."

Griff leaned closer to Brulard and whispered, "Are we talking about the same thing?"

Surreptitiously watching them through a hole drilled in the side of a municipal work truck was Hessler.

While they were conferring, the dog had moved on. Noticing this, it dawned on them that this was a dead end, and they tried to extricate themselves from the prostitute's clutches but did not succeed before she'd abused them verbally and physically. Freed at last, they took off after the dog.

After they had gone, another man approached the prostitute, linked arms with her, and proceeded with her down the street. It was Borisenko's aide, Grubov.

A group of Hare Krishna chanters in pale orange sheets moved along in a slow procession. The last chanter handed out leaflets to passers-by, smiling beatifically at everyone. When the dog bounded up to him and licked his hand, Griff and Brulard waded through the group and approached the man.

"Lippet," Brulard said.

"Peace and love," the man replied.

"Bullshit," Griff said. "Where's the stuff?"

Brulard tugged at Griff's arm, indicating that the dog had moved on again. "False alarm."

They followed wearily.

The Hare Krishna chanter looked after them until unseen arms from Hessler's truck dragged him inside.

In the same dark room where the film of Martinson's restaurant meeting with Borisenko was shown, several projected slides were now being carefully scrutinized. One of them showed Griff and Brulard talking to the redheaded woman. The second showed Griff and Brulard in the midst of the group of Hare Krishna chanters. The men who studied the photographs chattered incomprehensibly. The head chatterer was Chinese agent Chang.

Martinson and Hessler stood atop the Arc de Triomphe, talking in hushed tones, as if surrounded by listeners, although they were quiet alone.

"The religious nut is just a religious nut," Hessler reported. "The street cleaner they talked to is just a street cleaner."

"What about all the others they've contacted?" Martinson asked, but Hessler only shrugged.

"And another thing. We're not getting much response to those wedding invitations."

"It's August, sir. A lot of people are away."

"I want that church filled, Hessler. Even if it means inviting some of our own men."

"Yes, sir," Hessler whispered.

"And I want some royalty at that ceremony. I am not a man to be taken lightly. I am important. Get on to some of those kings and emperors we bailed out."

"I don't know," Hessler replied hesitantly. "Maybe the King of Swobodia would come."

"That old deadbeat? We can do better than that. I'm depending on you, Hessler."

"I'll try, sir."

"I hope you'll do a better job than you did today."

"But all the people they talked to were clean," Hessler protested.

"They must be up to something," Martinson said. "They've run the whole goddam length of the city."

"Maybe they're trying to throw us off the scent?" Hessler suggested hopefully.

"What scent?"

"I don't know, sir. Maybe they've just flipped out on us."

"No!" Martinson insisted. "They've got something. Moscow's authorized Borisenko to pay them up to a quarter of a million for it."

Hessler whistled appreciatively.

"Exactly."

"Why don't you just let me kill them now?" Hessler asked eagerly.

"Not until we find out what they've got."

Borisenko sat in an outdoor café, at an isolated table with a view of the Arc de Triomphe. From a transistor radio disguised as a cigarette pack came Martinson and Hessler's conversation, loud and clear.

Borisenko switched it off impatiently, checked his watch, and then saw a disheveled Grubov coming toward his table from the street.

"The prostitute is only a prostitute," Grubov said, wearily sinking into a chair.

"Martinson knows about my instructions from Moscow," Borisenko said, pointing to the cigarette pack.

"They've bugged the Kremlin?"

"They bug everything," Borisenko said with disgust. "My place . . . your place. . . . I'll bet they even bugged that prostitute's place."

Grubov smiled at the little joke, but when Borisenko turned around to signal the waiter, a guilty expression came over his face.

Chapter Fifteen

GRIFF AND BRULARD continued to trail the dog around the streets of Paris into the night. They were exhausted but Archie trotted merrily along. They stopped at the entrance to an alley down which the dog had turned, and leaned against the building.

"What's up there?" Griff asked, gesturing toward the alley.

"Dead end."

"Then what'd he go up there for?"

"Guess," Brulard said, and they both slumped into squatting positions.

"Nothing but a wild goose chase. He hasn't got any contacts."

"Then the stuff must be on him," Griff insisted.

"It isn't. We looked."

Brulard stood up and looked impatiently down the alley.

"Come on!" he called to the dog. "Shake a leg."

"It's gotta be on him . . ." Griff said, ". . . or *in* him."

"A capsule?"

"Of course! Lippet fed it to him in London. How long does it take for . . ." Words failed him and he was reduced to making a vague gesture.

"I'm not sure. But there was this Arab that tried to smuggle some dope out of Yemen. He had a camel swallow it in a capsule."

"And how long did that take?"

"It didn't. The capsule broke halfway down and the camel was on a trip for weeks."

"But if Lippet fed it to him yesterday . . ."

Reluctantly they looked up the alley as the dog returned.

"You'd better check it out," Griff said.

"*You* check it out."

"Call!" Griff said, and they threw fingers. Brulard grinned victoriously. Griff sighed disgustedly. "Got some matches?"

Brulard handed over a pack, and Griff stepped gingerly into the alley, carrying a piece of wood. Except for a rapid succession of match flares, accompanied by groans of revulsion, all was dark and quiet.

"You find it?" Brulard called out.

"Jesus," Griff muttered from the darkness.

"What's the matter?"

"He ain't the first! It's like a goddam mine field."

Brulard waited in silence, looking up and down the street for anyone who may have been following them, and absently stroking the dog's head.

"Hurry up!"

"How do I know which is his?"

"Play it safe," Brulard called back. "Take it all."

Playing it safe was also playing it dirty, and they took piles of the stuff back to Sybil's apartment.

"I am broad-minded, but this is ridiculous," she said, pacing the room in front of Paul and Gaspar who were busy at their usual task. "Keeping the poor little thing out all day . . . coming back with all . . ."

"It's a long story," Griff said, scraping his shoes.

"Long and sick," Sybil said.

"They promise a hundred thousand dollars," Gaspar

muttered from the table. "And they bring back a pile of . . ."

"Nothing!" Brulard said, standing in the bedroom doorway peeling off a pair of rubber gloves.

"You sure?" Griff asked.

"Positive."

"It's gotta be," Griff insisted.

"Go look for yourself," Brulard said, motioning toward the bathroom.

"Fascists!" Paul shouted.

"Lunatics!" Sybil accused.

"Shit mongers!" Gaspar yelled.

"We'd better do this scientifically," Griff said, delighted to have had an idea. He turned toward the dog but Sybil interposed.

"Do what scientifically?" she challenged. "What do you want from him?"

Griff didn't tell her. But she wanted the hundred thousand he'd promised her and she relented. He and Brulard left with the dog.

They found the nearest veterinarian's office and brought the dog in for an emergency appointment.

The vet ran the dog through the fluoroscope, and the three men studied the canine skeleton, looking for the elusive capsule.

"A large object, you say?" the vet asked.

"Uh . . . pretty large," Brulard replied evasively.

"And you're sure he swallowed it?"

"Pretty sure," Griff said.

The vet peered intently at the fluoroscope, shaking his head.

"Nothing in the esophagus."

"How about further down?" Brulard suggested.

"The stomach is clear. And the intestines. No, no obstructions."

"Not even a little tiny one?" Brulard asked.

"None at all. This is a very healthy dog."

"Yeah," Griff said. "Great."

"Except for the left eye, of course."

"Eye?" Brulard said.

"Yes, I thought I'd tested everything—gorillas with hernias, bats who couldn't fly—but this is the first animal I have ever seen with a contact lens."

"Lens?" Griff exclaimed.

"Oh, you mean the *lens*," Brulard said, and in the darkness tiptoed up to the dog.

"Yeah," Griff said. "It's funny about that. He kept bumping into things . . . you know . . . lamp posts, fire hydrants . . ."

Brulard grabbed the dog away from the machine. The frightened animal barked in alarm. Griff kept talking to distract the vet.

"So we took him to this optician . . ."

"Hold still, goddammit!" Brulard muttered as the dog squirmed in his arms.

"Only twenty-eighty in his left eye. And he couldn't walk around with granny glasses, could he?"

Brulard came up to him with the dog under one arm. In his other hand he gingerly held the contact lens.

"Got it," he said triumphantly, and the two of them spirited the dog out of the office.

The vet stood still for a moment, puzzled, then walked to the door and called out after them.

"But how did he read the eye chart?"

Chapter Sixteen

AFTER AN UNCOMFORTABLE night in Sybil's crowded quarters, they left early for a science equipment supply store, one that carried microscopes, telescopes, and complex lenses. The salespeople were occupied, so Griff and Brulard feverishly searched the display cases for something that would magnify the contact lens.

The first microscope they tried proved to be a disappointment.

"I can't make it out," Brulard said. "This thing's not strong enough."

A dignified clerk came up behind them and spoke. "May I help you gentlemen?"

"Yes," Griff said, rising to the occasion. "This is Professor Von Kleinst of the Von Kleinst Institute."

Brulard made a quick bow from the waist.

"He's looking for a very powerful microscope."

"Yes sir," the clerk said, gesturing toward the row of microscopes. "Any of these . . ."

"Nein!" Brulard had adopted a German accent. "Too dinky . . . teeny-weeny. . . . Need much more gross!"

"Ah," the clerk said, nodding with new understanding. "I know."

He led them to the back of the store "The Langendorf 2000."

"Lagendorf is maken a 2000?" Brulard said incredulously.

"A fantastic instrument," the clerk said as they approached a huge microscope. "It has given a perfectly clear image of a flea's ovaries."

Brulard stroked his chin, nodding approvingly.

"Why don't you try it, Professor?" Griff asked and shoved Brulard at the microscope.

"I'll get a slide," the clerk said but Griff stopped him.

"Never mind," he said. "He always carries his own."

Griff placed the lens under the microscope as Brulard looked through the eyepiece.

"How is it?" Griff asked anxiously.

Brulard was focusing frantically, shouting.

"Ach! Neine can see *anything."*

"First you must turn it on, *monsieur,"* the clerk said and switched on the light.

Griff smiled at the clerk, trying to recover their credibility.

"All the instruments at the Institute are automatic."

Brulard squinted into the eyepiece and focused more carefully.

"Well, Professor?" Griff asked. "What do you think?"

"Holy shit!"

Brulard embraced Griff and whooped with joy.

"He likes it," Griff told the clerk sheepishly, and steered Brulard toward the front of the store.

"What is it?" he whispered.

Brulard looked around, checking that they couldn't be overheard.

"The whole Russian network in China."

"You sure? Whew."

"Every spook agent they got there. Names and addresses."

The clerk had followed them to the door.

"Well, we'll let you know," Griff said and they left the store, gleefully smug.

"Martinson will pay plenty for this," Brulard said.

"Not as much as Borisenko," Griff said, holding up the lens and looking at it with adoration. "You beautiful . . . mmmm . . ."

He moved as if to plant a big kiss on the lens but Brulard grabbed his wrist.

"Don't! You'll smear it."

Griff nodded and tucked the contact lens back into the envelope. They parted and Brulard went off to negotiate with Borisenko while Griff returned to Sybil's for a nap.

When he awoke a few hours later, Sybil, Paul, and Gaspar were loading bombs into their knapsacks and suitcases. The dog sat on the table and watched them.

"Off to do your good deed for the day?" Griff asked. "Where's the lucky place?"

"It will all be told in our newspaper," Paul said, hoisting his knapsack on his back.

"With your circulation, it'll still be a secret."

"You!!"

Paul grabbed a hand grenade from the arsenal. He was about to pull the pin with his teeth when Gaspar jumped him and held him back. Paul struggled against his friend's hold and screamed at Griff.

"Cynic! Car wrecker!"

"Not now," Gaspar said, panting with the exertion of holding Paul down.

"You'd better have the money tomorrow," Sybil said.

"Don't worry," Griff assured her. "We will have."

"I hope you don't," Paul raged. "Then I can kill you."

Gaspar released Paul and they started for the door, hoisting their knapsacks. Sybil threw a cautionary glance at Griff and followed. Just then the door was thrown open and Brulard hurried in.

"Off to do your good deed for today?"

Paul and Gaspar glared at him but Sybil pushed them out the door. She looked at Griff and Brulard, then crossed the room, picked up the dog protectively, and left the apartment.

"What did Borisenko say?" Griff asked anxiously.

"Terrible things. But he upped it to three hundred thousand."

"We've done it!"

Brulard nodded, crossed the room and flattened himself against the wall to peer sideways out of the window. "He's waiting for us to name the place."

"What's the matter?"

"I keep feeling I'm being followed."

"Borisenko's men?"

"It feels more like Martinson's."

"Then we'd better meet Borisenko where Martinson can't break it up."

"Yeah," Brulard agreed, "but where?"

Several places were named before a desperate but perfect solution presented itself.

Chapter Seventeen

THE DAY OF Ellie Martinson's wedding turned out to be a beautiful one. Cars and limousines jammed the streets around the church. Chauffeurs idled about the parked limousines exchanging chatter about the people they drove for.

The guests wore formal daytime attire; men in gray cutaways with vests, striped trousers, silk ascots, and top hats; women in long gowns and matching large-brimmed hats. At the church entrance the verger checked their invitations.

A car screeched to a stop before the church, and Hessler jumped out. He ran to the entrance and tried to squeeze past the guests. The verger noticed him and barred the way.

"Your invitation, *monsieur?*"

Hessler stopped and searched his pockets frantically.

"I forgot it," he said, pushing the verger.

"You must have an invitation, *monsieur.*"

"I have to see Mr. Martinson," Hessler insisted. "It's urgent."

The verger shook his head while Hessler trembled with urgency and frustration.

"Listen," he said. "You . . . if it wasn't for me, the invitations wouldn't have been sent out."

"Sorry, *monsieur,*" the verger said, politely remaining firm.

Hessler backed off, muttering to himself, and looked for another way to get to Martinson.

The guests turned at the roaring of a souped-up motor, and were delighted to see the groom pull up in his sports car.

Alan reached around for his top hat and jumped out of the car. He walked to the back, hung a card on the rear bumper, and headed for the church. The sign read: JUST MARRIED.

The distraction of Alan's arrival provided Hessler with the chance he needed, and he ducked around the side of the church to find another way in. He searched furtively among the plantings until he came to a basement window. The window gave when he poked it with the tip of his shoe, so he squatted down and pried it open.

In a small room off the chapel, the bride waited. She pirouetted in front of Martinson, showing off her wedding gown.

"Beautiful," Martinson said adoringly. "A regular vision in white."

Ellie smiled back, but her smile faded.

"The only thing is . . ."

"What?"

"I don't think you like Alan."

"Of course I do," Martinson said through gritted teeth. "He's a fine boy."

"But do you think it's right for me to marry someone who despises you?"

"He does?" Martinson asked, not really surprised. He tried to laugh and sputtered. "Still, I don't have to live with him, do I?"

"You know what he said yesterday?"

"No. And I don't want to know. This is our big day, Ellie. I'm not letting him spoil it."

He took her hands and brought her closer to him.

"Now I've got a little surprise for you. Guess who's coming to your wedding?"

Ellie's eyes lit up. "Mother!"

"No, not your mother," he said, forcefully. "The King of Swobodia."

"The king?" Ellie said uncertainly.

"With four of his wives."

"But why would he travel all that way?"

"He didn't have to," Martinson explained. "He's in exile here."

"But why would he come to my wedding?"

"Because he knows me. That's the kind of circle your father moves in. Besides, he likes weddings." He added, as if it were an afterthought, "He's been married twenty-six times."

Ellie hesitated, then smiled broadly and threw her arms around her father.

"Oh, Daddy! A real king!"

"That puts the frosting on the cake, huh? I told you—this is going to be a wedding to remember."

The guests were still pouring in, still having their invitations checked. Some of the men looked distinctly uncomfortable dressed formally, as if leather jackets might have suited them better.

"Invitations," the verger called out politely as the guests milled in. "Invitations, please . . ."

Griff and Brulard moved with the crowd, their heads low, their faces hidden under the shadows of their top hats.

"Give him the invitations," Griff said as they neared the verger.

"Right. Got 'em here somewhere."

He went through the motions of checking for the invitations, stalling for time. The crowd was pushing them forward and at any moment they would be face to face with the demanding verger.

Suddenly a loud "oooooh" rose up, and everyone turned around. Griff and Brulard turned just long enough to ascertain that it was the King of Swobodia being helped from his limousine that had caused the stir. His four wives followed dutifully behind him.

Griff and Brulard took advantage of the old king's entrance and slid past the preoccupied verger into the church.

In the meantime, Hessler had squeezed through the basement window and landed noisily, catching his coat sleeve in the process and leaving it behind. He cursed under his breath and stood still while his eyes adjusted to the dark.

Griff and Brulard entered a pew to one side of the church and slumped down in an effort to be inconspicuous. Under cover of their top hats, they cast anxious glances about and spoke in whispers.

"I still don't know if this was the best place," Brulard said.

"What could be safer? Martinson wouldn't pull anything at his own daughter's wedding. And Borisenko won't try anything because he doesn't want to antagonize Martinson."

Brulard nodded uncertainly and Griff nodded back.

Each felt a hand on his shoulder and they turned, prepared for flight or fight. They sighed in relief to discover two old women behind them who pointed disapprovingly at their top hats. The two men apologized and removed their hats, slouching down lower.

Suddenly the first chord of the organ was heard. A

hush fell over the assembled guests as the priest came out in his vestments and walked slowly to the altar.

The wedding party waited at the rear of the church. The bridesmaids and flower girls, with Alan and his best man, stood nervously at the center aisle. Martinson and Ellie came out of the small waiting room, and Ellie smiled at both the men in her life.

The flower girls started forward at the head of the procession, strewing petals. As Ellie began up the aisle with her father, the two bridesmaids picked up the train of her gown. Martinson turned around and whispered fiercely at them. "Move over! Don't stand behind me!"

One moved quickly, frightened, and bumped the other. Martinson sighed and turned around, put on the face of the proud father and moved forward with Ellie.

Just before Alan followed, he took a wad of gum from his mouth and stuck it on the back of the last pew.

Outside, two identical Citroëns pulled up and one discharged Borisenko, dressed in morning clothes and carrying a huge sterling silver samovar with gift wrapping on its handles. Grubov and another Russian agent, both in morning clothes, emerged from the other car.

When the three Russians approached the already closed door, the watchful verger was preparing the collection boxes. He looked up at them disapprovingly and extended his hand. "Your invitations, please."

"Would we be dressed like this if we didn't have invitations?" Borisenko asked.

"Then if I may have them?"

Borisenko gestured to Grubov, "Give it to him."

Grubov stepped forward, touching his pockets, then jammed his fist into the verger's stomach. The other agent clamped his hand over the verger's mouth, and they dragged him to the stairway inside the church, just outside the chapel door.

Inside the chapel, the wedding procession had reached the altar, the organ music had stopped and the priest had begun the ceremony.

Griff and Brulard shielded their faces with their prayer books and looked stealthily around for Borisenko.

The King of Swobodia wept silently.

A rear door opened and Hessler emerged, his clothes smudged with coal, the right sleeve of his jacket missing completely. He spotted Martinson at the altar, and getting down on all fours, he began crawling up the center aisle toward his boss.

The ceremony was proceeding with dignity and Martinson was feeling very proud of himself. Out of the corner of his eye he perceived some motion and then felt a tugging at his sleeve. He jumped back instinctively and found Hessler at his feet.

"They made a deal for three hundred thousand," Hessler said, too loudly, given the circumstances.

His voice was loud enough for the priest to have heard and the ceremony stopped. Martinson smiled, motioned for the priest to continue, and hissed back at Hessler.

"Where are they now?"

"I don't know."

"Find out."

Hessler nodded and started crawling back up the

aisle. Martinson looked nervously at the retreating form, checked his watch, and turned to the priest.

"Can't we go a little faster. We haven't got all week."

He ignored the incredulous stares of Ellie and Alan and gestured to the priest. "Faster! Faster!"

The priest continued the ceremony in double time.

As Hessler reached the back of the church, the rear door opened, and Borisenko came in clutching the large silver samovar. Hessler hid himself in a pew, breathing heavily, then peeked out.

Borisenko selected a seat on a side aisle. A moment later Grubov and the other agent entered and joined Borisenko in the pew.

Brulard spotted the Russians and alerted Griff, who made his way to the aisle crawling along the floor.

The priest was reciting the ceremony with lightning speed, and Martinson was slightly relieved, until he felt the now-familiar tug at his sleeve.

"Later," Martinson whispered.

"Look!" Hessler said urgently.

Martinson turned and his face froze.

"What's he doing here?" he said aloud.

All eyes in the church turned toward him, and the priest stopped his frantic chanting.

"He wasn't invited!" Martinson said in the same loud voice.

"Shh," the best man hissed.

"Shh yourself," Martinson said and turned to Hessler. "Watch Borisenko."

Hessler nodded and crawled away up the aisle. The priest began intoning the ceremony even more rapidly. Before Hessler had gone far, he saw Griff moving toward Borisenko, so he retreated and poked Martinson's leg. Martinson turned and Hessler directed his glance. He made a gesture to Hessler and turned to the priest, looking annoyed and frantic.

"Slow down, will you? Slowly! Slowly!"

The priest shook his head in confusion and stopped completely.

"Daddy, please," Ellie pleaded.

"Well, what's his hurry? Where's the fire? Slowly," he said; and when the priest began reciting in a drawl, Martinson nodded in approval.

Borisenko feigned interest in the ceremony and did not take his eyes from the altar even after Griff had joined him in the pew.

"You have it?" Borisenko asked Griff without looking at him.

"You have the money?"

"Let's see it."

"Let's see the money."

Borisenko opened the samovar and tipped it so Griff could see that the money was inside. He closed it quickly.

Griff nodded his approval, removed a small jeweler's case from his pocket, and flipped it open to reveal the contact lens.

"All right," Borisenko said, taking a jeweler's eyeglass from his inside pocket.

Griff in turn pulled a small, folded knapsack from inside his cutaway coat.

Hessler crawled to a pew behind them, squeezed himself in and watched.

Griff transferred the money into his knapsack as Borisenko studied the contact lens with his jeweler's glass.

"Fine," he said and snapped the case closed. "When you've finished, the samovar goes to the happy couple."

He got up, moved past Griff, and started out of the church. Grubov and the other agent followed as far as Griff's pew.

Hessler suddenly jumped atop his seat and pointed frantically to Borisenko. Several men, heeding Hessler's warning, rose and started up the aisles toward Borisenko.

Hearing the men behind him, the Russian blew into a small ultrasonic whistle that hung around his neck. The sound was unheard by everyone except his chauffeur, who signaled the other Russians in the cars, and they all headed for the church.

The priest continued the ceremony, undaunted by the commotion at the back of his church. Borisenko backed down the aisle carefully. Griff continued the transfer of money with such concentration that he didn't notice Grubov and the other Russian agent descending on him from opposite sides of his pew. Brulard saw them and stood up.

"Griff!"

He looked up and saw Grubov coming at him. He swung the samovar at the Russian, but missed, and it crashed against the wooden pew. Grubov managed to grab the other handle, and he and Griff played tug of war with it.

The rear door flew open, and the Russian agents came rushing in. When Griff saw them, he released his hold on the samovar, and Grubov, off balance, fell backward into the aisle. A Russian agent zeroed in to get the money. Griff saw him and lifted the knapsack.

"Catch!" he shouted to Brulard and heaved the sack at him. It fell short, landing on the head of the King of Swobodia, and Brulard leaped up to retrieve it.

At the same time, Borisenko directed his agents toward the knapsack, and they and Brulard all converged on the King of Swobodia.

Grubov staggered to his feet in the aisle, clutching the samovar, and pulled his gun. Borisenko grabbed his arm before he could fire.

"No guns. Just get the money back."

Grubov handed the samovar to Borisenko and rushed off to join the melee around the king.

Borisenko clutched the samovar to his chest, and sidled along the wall toward a rear exit door. He looked to see that he was unobserved, then slipped out of the church by way of the basement.

The King of Swobodia had been knocked out by the money-filled knapsack, and three of his wives were desperately trying to revive him. The fourth wife had the sack, but before she could open it, Brulard leaped over a final pew and grabbed it from her.

Two CIA men at the rear of the church drew their guns, but Hessler relayed Martinson's message.

"No shooting. Agreement of '72."

The CIA men nodded in disappointment and replaced their guns.

Brulard and Griff signaled to each other from opposite sides of the church and tried to meet. But the Russian agents blocked the center aisle while the CIA men had the side aisles covered.

Grubov and another Russian agent squirmed past the bewildered guests, fighting their way closer to Brulard. Just as Grubov made a lunge for him, Brulard tossed the knapsack across to Griff.

Hessler saw the toss from the back of the church and barged toward Griff, knocking people out of the way. Griff saw Hessler coming, signaled for Brulard, who was free from Grubov, and threw the sack back to him.

At the altar, the priest continued the ceremony, while Martinson's eyes frantically followed the knapsack's progress.

Martinson's panic perfectly complemented the unvarnished chaos in the church. The guests tried to follow the ceremony but were constantly being pushed around, stepped on, shoved, and knocked down.

Grubov forced his way out of the pew after Brulard, but upon reaching the aisle, he ran smack into two CIA men. He knocked one down immediately, then grappled on the floor with the other. Grubov seized the advantage and shoved both feet in the CIA man's stomach, sending him flying into the organist. A deafening boom resounded through the church.

The priest looked stricken and stopped the ceremony.

"Never mind!" Martinson screamed. "Keep going! Keep going!"

Griff and Brulard had worked their separate ways to the front pews and found themselves surrounded by CIA and Russian agents. Brulard was more tightly covered than Griff so he heaved the knapsack to Griff.

As Griff caught it, a Russian agent leaped up and grabbed for it. Griff pulled out his cigarette lighter and sprayed the man with LS-10. The agent immediately crumbled and fell on a stout lady in a straw hat.

Taking their cue from Griff, all of the agents whipped out their cigarette lighters and began spraying at each other over the heads of the guests.

In the ensuing pandemonium, Griff and Brulard made progress toward the altar, the knapsack securely clutched under Griff's arm.

The ceremony had ground to a halt again. The priest stared open-mouthed. Even the usually imperturbable Alan watched the proceedings with outraged amazement.

"What the hell's going on here?"

"Daddy," Ellie moaned tearfully. "Do something."

"Never mind," Martinson said and turned to the priest. "Keep going. Ask her if she'll take him . . ."

The confused priest nodded and began again.

"Do you . . . Eleanor Jane Martinson . . . ?"

"Say 'I do,' " Martinson whispered to Ellie.

The King of Swobodia had finally recovered from the blow. He stood regally. A Russian agent on his right and a CIA man on his left squirted each other with LS-10. The king intercepted both squirts and went down for the second time.

By now, Borisenko had stumbled through the darkened basement, found the same window through which Hessler had entered the church, and squirmed out of it, covered in soot, the samovar clutched in his hand. He dashed to his waiting car, jumped in, and leaned forward.

"Let's go!" he ordered. "Hurry."

The car did not start and he poked the chauffeur. "Come on! Move!"

The chauffeur turned to face Borisenko. It was Chinese agent Chang.

Borisenko tried for one door, then the other, but each was blocked by a Chinese agent who got in. One of the agents lifted the jewelery case from Borisenko's pocket and handed it to Chang, who smiled and opened it calmly.

"No!" Borisenko shouted. "It's nothing. It's all lies!" He was silenced as the car drove off.

The doors of the church were flung open and the

guests poured out, staggering and falling, banging into each other, formal suits and dresses crumpled and torn, their faces red and puffy from the LS-10.

Inside the church Griff and Brulard pushed through some dazed guests who were still struggling out, and met in the center aisle.

"Follow me!" Griff shouted, handing over the knapsack.

At the altar, the befuddled priest was completing the ceremony.

"I now pronounce you man and wife," he said with great relief.

Martinson turned to Ellie and prodded her with an anxious finger. "Kiss him," he told her and looked to Alan. "Kiss her," he told his new son-in-law and shoved the two of them together. As they kissed, Martinson spun around to face the congregation.

"Hessler!" he called, pointing to the departing Griff and Brulard. "Stop them!"

Griff and Brulard were almost home free when Hessler appeared, barring their way. Griff took out his cigarette lighter, but Hessler batted it away, spraying his own instead. Griff ducked, and the spray caught Brulard full in the face. While Hessler gloated, Griff caught him on the jaw with a fist. Hessler went down and Griff ran past him out of the church.

He hopped into the first car he saw. It was Alan's sports car, bearing the JUST MARRIED sign. Griff started the motor and looked back to see a stumbling Brulard just barely out of the church.

"Here!" Griff yelled to him, waving his arms.

Brulard saw him and tried to maneuver toward the sports car, but his legs were rubbery and he moved uncertainly. The precious knapsack dangled unnoticed from his arm. Griff continued to rev up the engine, watching Brulard's drugged progress with growing impatience and alarm.

"Come on!" he shouted encouragingly.

Martinson, Hessler, and two other CIA men rushed out of the church and moved on Brulard, shoving people aside in their frantic effort to get the knapsack.

"Come on boy!" Griff called, urging him on. "You can make it. Keep going!"

Brulard redoubled his efforts, but his movements were still faltering.

"Throw it!" Griff yelled and Brulard reared back to hurl the knapsack.

Just then Martinson and Hessler grabbed him while the other CIA men ran to the sports car. Seeing that there was no way to rescue Brulard, Griff threw the car into first gear and shot off.

Martinson and Hessler dragged Brulard and the money into another car and took off, sending a huge cloud of dust over the guests. When the dust began to settle, a lone figure emerged, staggering blindly toward the church, a sterling silver samovar jammed over his head.

"Grubov!" Borisenko shouted from inside the samovar. "Where are you?"

Grubov and another Russian agent rushed to their leader's aid. Each secured a hold on a handle of the samovar and pulled mightily. A roar of anguish reverberated inside the pot.

That was all that was left of the wedding, which had been a memorable one indeed.

Chapter Eighteen

IN THE BASEMENT of the building that housed the Four Corners Travel Agency, Sybil, Paul, and Gaspar were busy at their chosen profession. Sybil looked at a detailed drawing of the building's structure and gave silent instructions to tape the explosives to the beams that supported the building. Other explosives were already in place, and the dog wagged his tail as the last bomb was taped to the last beam.

Several stories above them, in Martinson's private office stockroom, Brulard was seated on a straight-backed chair, head lolling and eyes glazed, still under the influence of LS-10. Martinson stared at him impatiently, then shattered the silence of the room by slapping him in the face.

"Talk!" he screamed. "Start talking, Brulard. What was on those microdots?"

He slapped him again, and still Brulard did not talk.

"Talk!"

Brulard's eyes opened blearily, he smiled to himself and began to sing.

"Shine on . . . shine on harvest moon . . ."

"See," Martinson said approvingly to Hessler and Evans. "Our training works. Whenever you're being tortured, think song titles."

121

"But he isn't being tortured."

"Not yet. But he knows he will be. Don't you, Brulard? You know we'll stop at nothing, don't you? So
make it easy on yourself, boy. We're on the same side.
Come on . . . tell us about the microdots . . ."

"Down by the old mill stream . . ."

"Shut up! Forget your goddam training for a minute. Tell you what we'll do. We're going to let you
keep all the money . . . all that gorgeous money . . .
if you'll just tell us . . ."

"Yes sir, that's my baby . . . no sir, I don't mean
maybe . . ."

Sybil's apartment was empty when Griff burst in.
He slammed the door, went to the closet to change,
and saw a pile of dynamite in the corner. A plan began to formulate in his mind.

"The bells are ringing for me and my gal . . . the
birds are singing . . ."

"That's enough!" Martinson shouted in exasperation
and slapped him again.

Hessler hooked up a lethal-looking electronic device.
It had three cables, one of which was secured to
Brulard's head, the others clamped to his wrists.

"We don't want to hurt you, boy," Martinson said.
"You know that. Don't force us. Be reasonable."

"Roll out the barrel . . ."

"No, no, no, boy. Not that one. Think of your
country. Think of America the Beautiful."

He stood at attention before Brulard, and as he sang
Hessler and Evans joined in.

"For purple mountain's majesty . . . above the
fruited plain . . . America, America, God shed his
grace on thee . . ."

"All the Russian agents in China," Brulard said.

"What? What'd you say?"

"The microdots," Brulard said, head still lolling, eyes still glazed, "have all the names of all the Russian agents in China."

Martinson stared for a moment, then slapped Brulard hard across the face.

"Liar! You think I'd swallow that? We trained him to lie good, didn't we, Hessler? Now Brulard . . . it was 'Crossroads.' Or 'Fusebox,' right?"

Brulard said nothing. Martinson shook him by the shoulders.

"Was it 'Fusebox'?"

"The names of all the Russian . . ."

Martinson slapped him again before he could complete the sentence.

"For the last time. The truth . . . or we throw the switch."

Hessler gripped the switch on the cables leading to Brulard's head and wrists.

"Fluent in seven languages, eh? One jolt from this and you'll speak them all at the same time. Now talk!"

"The names of all the Russian . . ."

"Throw the switch, Hessler."

As Hessler's hand started fo move, the door from the bathroom was flung open by Griff.

"Hold it!"

His morning coat hung open to reveal a belt of bombs. Griff held a fuse menacingly in his hand.

"Grab him!" Martinson ordered, and Hessler and Evans went into motion.

"Watch it!" Griff warned, caressing the fuse. "One yank on this and we all go up."

Hessler and Evans stepped back.

"That's better," Griff said. "Over there."

He began to free Brulard.

"And we'll take the money while we're at it, Martinson."

"Griff, this is silly. You wouldn't blow yourself up."

"Wouldn't I? Just try me. Come on now, the money."

"Give it to him, Hessler."

"No!" Hessler said, grabbing the knapsack of money and backing away. "He's bluffing. He hasn't got the guts."

"Ten seconds, Hessler," Griff warned. "Nine . . . eight . . ."

"You're faking," Hessler insisted. "You've always been a fake."

"Seven . . . six . . ."

"Give it to him!" Martinson ordered.

"Five . . . four . . . three . . ."

"Go on. Pull the string."

"Two . . ."

"That's an order, Hessler!" Martinson bellowed.

"Go on," Hessler said to Griff. "I dare you. Fake."

"Listen, you . . ."

Griff moved toward Hessler, holding his fist up threateningly. As he raised his hand the fuse jerked, and Evans and Martinson ducked. Griff looked at them uncomprehendingly for a second, then looked down at his hand.

"Boom," he said sheepishly.

"I told you!" Hessler cried victoriously.

"Get him, men," Martinson ordered and they converged on Griff.

"Happy birthday to you . . ." Brulard sang on undaunted.

"Boom, huh?" Martinson said.

Griff was within their grasp when the building was

jolted by a tremendous explosion. Part of the ceiling rained down, plaster crumbled about them, and dust filled the air. A wall gaped open into the next room. In the settling smoke several things were revealed. Through the broken wall a tape recorder could be seen spinning, while a movie camera chugged away filming everything. An assortment of powerful microphones dangled from the damaged ceiling.

Martinson waded through the debris, but he was too slow and Griff and Brulard managed to escape.

"They're getting away. Stop them. They've got 'Crossroads.' I never liked 'Crossroads' . . . or 'Fusebox.' I've got tapes to prove it. I just went along. I'll get immunity. Yes, immunity. I've got the tapes!"

Hessler looked up from the floor where he was pinned under half the ceiling, and wondered how he could get immunity himself. Just following orders; he'd try that one.

Griff and Brulard had charged through the maze of littered rooms and squeezed out a broken window to the street, still in their morning coats.

They happened upon Sybil, Paul, and Gaspar who were making their getaway.

Griff dangled the knapsack of money, and he and Brulard had no trouble at all getting a lift.

Chapter Nineteen

THE PEUGEOT BOUNCED merrily through the lovely French countryside. The money had improved everyone's disposition and relieved much tension. The atmosphere in the car was actually pleasant.

"Eighty-seven," Brulard mumbled, counting the cash. "Eighty-eight . . . eighty-nine . . . ninety thousand . . . ninety-one . . ."

But the car began pulling to the right, and a thumping sound could be heard. *"Merde,"* said Gaspar as he pulled over. He got out, saw a flat tire, and kicked the car.

The others got out too, relieved to find nothing serious. Gaspar cursed as he opened the trunk and rummaged through the unused explosives for some tools. He was having difficulties.

But Sybil was the happiest she'd been in days, and she played joyfully with the dog.

Griff and Brulard had been looking forward to a breather. They reclined on the grass and shared a bottle of wine.

Even the usually taciturn Paul was elated, dancing by himself on the grass.

Gaspar removed the blown-out tire, and Paul picked it up and tossed it lightly into the trunk. A sudden distinctly ominous buzzing followed the impact.

Griff and Brulard thought nothing of it until they saw the three bombers freeze in terror.

"The money!" Paul shrieked. Gaspar pulled him away, and they flattened themselves. Following their lead, Griff and Brulard hit the ground and buried their heads. The next moment, the car exploded.

The two men stood up, shrugged, brushed the grass from their morning suits, and started down the road for another hitch. A battle raged among the anarchists. But that was behind them.

Griff began humming, and Brulard easily picked up the tune.

"Oh we ain't got a barrel of money . . . Maybe we're ragged and funny . . . But we'll travel along, singing a song, side by side."